SEA FISHES & INVERTEBRATES
OF THE NORTH SEA
& ENGLISH CHANNEL

LAWSON WOOD

First published in 2008 by
New Holland Publishers (UK) Ltd
London • Cape Town • Sydney • Auckland

www.newhollandpublishers.com

Garfield House, 86–88 Edgware Road, London W2 2EA,
United Kingdom

80 McKenzie Street, Cape Town 8001, South Africa

Unit 1, 66 Gibbes Street, Chatswood, New South
Wales, Australia 2067

218 Lake Road, Northcote, Auckland, New Zealand

10 9 8 7 6 5 4 3 2 1

ISBN 978 1 84773 125 8

Senior Editor: Krystyna Mayer
Design: D & N Publishing
Cartography: Stephen Dew
Production: Melanie Dowland
Commissioning Editor: Simon Papps
Editorial Direction: Rosemary Wilkinson

Reproduction by Modern Age Repro House Ltd,
   Hong Kong
Printed and bound in Malaysia by Times Offset (M)
   SDN Bhd

CONTENTS

The North Sea 4
Fish Identification Groups 19

PLANTS

- Seagrasses 22
- Algae 22

INVERTEBRATES

- Sponges 32
- Cnidarians 36
- Bryozoans 52
- Worms 54
- Crustaceans 60
- Molluscs 74
- Echinoderms 92
- Ascidians 98

FISHES

- Sharks 102
- Rays 104
- Salmon 104
- Conger Eels 104
- Pipefishes 106
- Sticklebacks 106
- Gurnards 106

- Flounders and Flatfishes 108
- Anglerfishes 110
- Scorpionfishes 110
- Hooknoses 110
- Dragonets 112
- Suckerfishes 112
- Cod and Bass 114
- Mackerel 116
- Mullet 116

- Weaverfishes 116
- Wrasses 118
- Gobies 120
- Blennies 120
- Wolf Fishes 122
- Sunfishes 122

OTHER VERTEBRATES

- Turtles 124
- Cetaceans 124
- Seals 124

Index 126
Acknowledgements 128

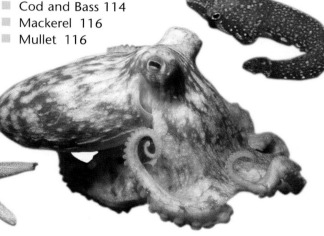

Marine National Parks

1. Nationalpark Niedersachsisches Wattenmeer
2. Nationalpark Hamburgisches Wattenmeer
3. Nationalpark Holsteinisches Wattenmeer
4. Nationalpark Vorpommersche Baddenlandschaft
5. Nationalpark Jasmund
6. Schiermonnikog National Park
7. St Abbs & Eyemouth Marine Nature Reserve

Faeroe Is.

Shetland Is.

NORWAY

SWEDEN

Pentland Firth   *Orkney Is.*

SCOTLAND

Kristiansand •

Skagarrak

Kattegat

Tay

Devil's Hole

North Sea

Forth

7 •Eyemouth

DENMARK

Farne Is.

Hebrides

British Isles

Dogger Bank

3

2

4 **5**

6 **1**

IRELAND

Humber

ENGLAND

WALES

The Wash

THE NETHERLANDS

Ems

Elbe

Thames

Godwin Sands

Dover Straits

•Ostende

Rhine

GERMANY

BELGIUM

English Channel

Channel Is.

Normandy

Seine

Brittany

Baie du Mont St Michel

FRANCE

0   250 km

THE NORTH SEA

My introduction to the North Sea came as a young lad growing up on the coast of the fishing village of Eyemouth in the south-east of Scotland. My youth was spent exploring rockpools, collecting shells on the beach, and snorkeling along the coast and even in some of the larger rockpools. Early teens brought the first exploration with SCUBA in 1965. By 1970 I was taking a camera underwater and recording the fantastic creatures that I had grown up to love. Included in this guide are just a few of the many and varied creatures that inhabit the shores of the North Sea: they are the most common species that are likely to be encountered.

A SEA OF SEAS

From Brittany to the Baltic and Normandy to Norway, from the Flemish lowlands to the deepwater fjords and Ostende to the Orkney Islands, the North Sea ebbs and flows four times daily, carrying a mind-boggling variety of animals and plants, and sustaining complex ecosystems from the upper shore down to the deepest depths of the 'Devil's Hole' in the central North Sea.

Many visitors to the North Sea are astonished at the great profusion of marine life that exists in this relatively small, box-like region bounded by the British Isles to the west and the shores of northern France, Belgium, the Netherlands, Denmark, Norway and southern Sweden to the east.

The habitats and the animals and plants that live on, in and around them are greatly influenced by the might of the Atlantic Ocean. Dividing in two when it reaches Ireland and the British Isles, a small current pushes through into the English Channel, aided by a current that sweeps up the coast of west Africa and catches planktonic creatures from the mouth of the Mediterranean Sea, across the deep Bay of Biscay and up north-western Europe. By far the greatest volume of water turns north along the west coast of Ireland and around the Hebrides, Orkney and Shetland, to combine with an Arctic current that sends millions of gallons of nutrient-rich water into the North Sea from a northerly direction. The North Sea is also connected to the Baltic Sea via the deepwater trench of the Skagarrak between Norway and Denmark, and the much shallower Kattegat between eastern Denmark and south-western Sweden.

The diversity of marine life found in the North Sea is vast, with a staggering number of invertebrates and fishes, as well as seals and otters, dolphins, porpoises and many other cetaceans, and seabirds in their countless thousands. Large, land-based seabird colonies are indicative of the profusion of fish to be found in certain areas, such as St Abbs Head and the Bass Rock in south-eastern Scotland. Razorbills, guillemots, puffins, shags, cormorants, fulmars, gannets, gulls and terns all feed on coastal fish stocks, and seals gather in river estuaries to harvest the migrating salmon and sea trout.

Humans have always harvested the sea – indeed, many small coastal communities still rely on the sea for their economy. It is said that for every person employed in the fishing industry at sea, another six people are employed on shore. Now we harvest not only fish stocks, but also collect shellfish – crabs, lobsters, shrimps and molluscs including razor shells, cockles, mussels and scallops – as well as algae for the pharmaceutical industry. Sadly, our species appears to be trying to take the last fishes from what was once thought to be an unlimited supply.

Herring Gull chick.

MAN'S IMPACT

In recent years, great emphasis has been placed on the rise of pollution, and the environmental impact of the chemical industry, oil and gas platforms, coastal erosion, coastal development and massive-scale reclamation of the sea.

The many rivers that flow into the North Sea – the Thames, Humber, Forth and Tay in the British Isles, and the Seine, Ems, Elbe and Rhine deltas in continental Europe – exert the greatest influence on its waters. Pollutants from the industrialized coastal communities flow down the rivers and can have devastating effects on sub-tidal habitats. Shipwrecks, oil spills, chemical leakage and more natural disasters such as landslides and vast flooding have also had profound effects on coastal habitats and the creatures that live around the shores, like seabirds, seals, otters and cetaceans – not forgetting the human population, which in some cases clings precariously to the edge of the sea.

Due largely to over-fishing, the vast shoals of herring that once shored up Britain's economy are no longer sustainable. Cod, Haddock and Saithe, the hunter–killers that once herded the herring, are also no longer viable for fishing. The North Sea's coastal governments have imposed restrictions on fish species caught and the amount of fishes that are allowed to be landed. These largely uninformed bureaucrats have not only failed to act in time, but also have no conception of the inter-relationships of the marine life. It is impossible to catch a particular species of fish or shellfish without catching others 'by catch' at the same time. This by catch is killed, too, and dumped unceremoniously overboard, which creates a multitude of other problems. Dumped by catch is not only an unnecessary waste of vital resources and marine species – the waste lands in a heap on the seabed, where existing sedentary marine life is smothered and killed by the rotting carcasses.

We have a curious imbalance in operation in many areas where wild species are under threat, yet fish farms are attempting to change the eating habits of the population by having salmon and bass more readily available. Sadly, it takes 3–4 tonnes of caught wild fishes to be processed into 1 tonne of fish meal for farmed fishes.

The Saithe is just one of the many species threatened by human activity.

THE BIRTH OF THE NORTH SEA

The land masses that border the North Sea are not fixed and many islands are in constant flux, with some parts eroding and those eroded parts being accumulated and built up elsewhere. The land and its coastline have changed remarkably over the millennia as the shifting tectonic plates have forever altered the planet.

In the Carboniferous period about 300–350 million years ago, the area now known as the North Sea was located slightly south of the equator and had tropical rainforests equivalent to the tropical Amazon basin. It is these ancient forests of giant ferns and hardwoods that were laid down and compressed by sedimentary mud and eventually formed the coal seams that stretch across this relatively modern sea.

Gradually, over millions of years, the European landmass moved northwards, and the climate around 240 million years ago during the Permian period was similar to that of the Persian Gulf. Under the baking sun, water evaporated almost as quickly as it was replenished from an open channel in the north of the region near present-day Norway. The resulting deposits of mineral salts led to the birth of the chemical industry in the 19th century. By the 20th century, geologists had discovered that the mineral salts capped giant reserves of natural gas, which had escaped from the much deeper coal seams. This discovery heralded the start of the North Sea gas-field industry.

Later, in the Jurassic period of around 168 million years ago, the North Sea was an amazing wilderness of deltas and debris fields incredibly rich in organic material. It is in these ancient deposits covered in impervious sedimentary mud and rocks that the North Sea oil lies.

By the time of the Cretaceous period around 120 million years ago, the north European region had moved 40 degrees north of the equator and, apart from the ancient and incredibly high peaks of Scandinavia, Scotland and Wales, the whole of north-western Europe was under a chalk sea. This chalk formation ceased around the same time that the dinosaurs became extinct. At this time the North Sea alternately dried up and flooded many times, and Britain was connected to mainland Europe or cast adrift several times.

In the Eocene epoch 45 million years ago, the land masses were pretty much formed and relative changes to the coastlines were a direct result of river run-off creating huge sediment fields and river deltas. Moving on to the last Ice Age 20,000 years ago, the advancing Arctic ice field was over 2km (1¼ miles) thick in some areas. Deep chasms were created in the North Sea, such as the Devil's Hole at over 300m (987ft) deep, and river drainage was forced south-west into the Atlantic basin, to the north of the present-day Channel Islands, an area now known as Hurd Deep.

North Sea coastal cliffs at St Abbs Head in south-east Scotland.

TIDES & CURRENTS

The Atlantic Ocean currents bring warm water, which transfers some of its heat into the prevailing westerly winds. As a consequence, north-western Europe is much warmer than its geographical counterparts such as Hudson Bay in northern Canada and southern Greenland, which freeze completely for months each year. The temperature of the North Sea is typically 5–10°C (41–50°F) all year round, with local anomalies dropping to as low as 3°C (37.4°F) during January and February, and rising to as high as 16°C (60.8°F) in August, September and early October.

The Atlantic current effectively splits in two when it reaches Ireland and the British Isles, and the two currents inevitably do not run at the same speed. One current pushes through the English Channel, while the other travels up the Western Isles and enters the North Sea from the north. Quite often the currents meet and cancel each other out. At other times they combine to make punishing tidal races, creating standing waves and huge whirlpools. Subsequently, the tidal range varies enormously, with less than 1m (3ft 3in) of change in northern Norway and an average of 6m (20ft) around the coast of Britain, to as much as 11m (37ft) in the Baie du Mont St Michel in north-western France.

The tidal currents in the southern North Sea flood southwards and ebb northwards. The maximum tidal current increases southwards, from approximately 1 knot in the north to 3 knots in the south. The tidal range follows a

Fisherman's hut made from an upturned boat.

similar pattern, increasing from 2m (6ft 6in) in the north to 5m (16ft 5in) in the south. In the latter area, tidal current speeds in the eastern English Channel increase in the Dover Straits due to the restriction of the channel and the presence of tidal sand ridges aligned with the direction of flow. The maximum speed of tidal streams at Dover is about 1.75m (5ft 9in) per second. As greatest tidal ranges tend to occur in narrow channels, it is not unusual for the range to reach 7m (23ft) in the Dover Straits and English Channel.

The tidal forces combined with the geographical and geological situation and historical influence generally dictate that the main tidal streams flow in an anti-clockwise direction in the North Sea. Coastal variations are fairly predictable, as are the levels of the tides in conjunction with the phases of the moon. However, the English Channel has its own particular, often-conflicting currents, which may vary from season to season. The confluence with the Baltic Sea has a deepwater current that flows east into the Baltic and a surface current of brackish water that flows west.

Eons of change have sculpted the seabed and greatly influenced the direction of the currents, yet the shifting Godwin Sands and Dogger Bank are testimony to the fact that you really cannot predict what these currents and tidal variations will do. Much of the sedimentation at these points is actually deposited from ancient ice flows and long-extinct river basins and deltas.

North Sea rough seas.

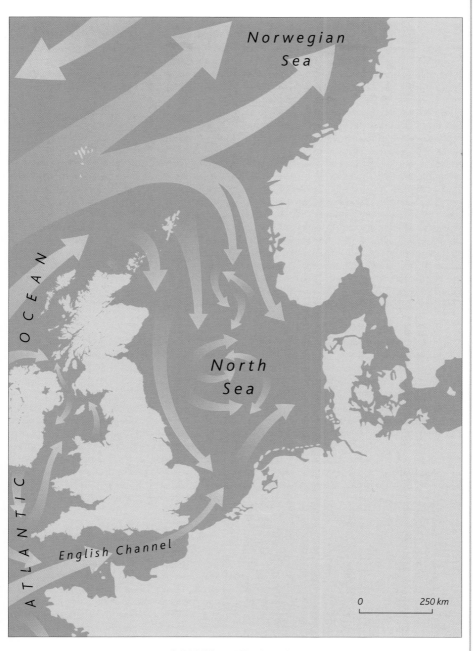

CURRENTS IN THE NORTH SEA

THE HABITATS

The first impression many people have of the North Sea is that of an empty expanse of waves rolling along and crashing on the shore. They are unaware of its hidden and remarkable charm, and of its huge diversity of marine life and often exotic colours. Depths in the North Sea vary from only a few tens of metres in the southern latitudes to over 200m (660ft) in the north. The various habitats are as diverse as those in any specialized environment and, although the area includes some very deep water sections and many commercial fishing grounds, the focus of this book is on the veneer that is visible while visiting this valuable resource, whether by scuba diving, snorkeling or rockpooling. One of the most obvious places to start in a hunt for marine life is the rockpools. Much of our knowledge about this aspect of the North Sea comes from the early Victorians, who explored and catalogued everything they could find fiercely and passionately.

ROCKPOOLS

These areas are found after a receding tide and are directly on the shoreline, known as the littoral zone. They are mini-oases of life akin to aquariums, but the creatures living within them are incredibly hardy, being able to withstand both rapid change of salinity (after heavy rainfall in a shallow pool) and differences in water temperature (for instance at the height of summer, when the water temperature in shallow pools can rise alarmingly for 6–8 hours before they are once more submerged by the advancing tide). Shallow pools usually contain several small beadlet anemones, several types of seaweed, and small blennies and tiny crabs, with the rocky exposed sides being grazed upon by limpets and periwinkles. Deeper pools are fringed with sturdier seaweeds and may contain juvenile Haddock, large Edible Crabs, lobster and even octopus.

ROCKY SHORES

These offer a firm substrate base for hardy algae and other, more sedentary forms of life to attach to. The particular selection of marine life here depends on the type of rock present. Some softer rocks can be bored into and therefore support more life than harder, glaciated granite rocks that offer few surfaces for animals to grip onto and thus only have a slight scattering of animal life. Exposed locations are always badly beaten by prevailing storms. These factors determine the types of marine life that can be sustained in a place. Chitons, urchins, limpets and barnacles are perhaps the most common rocky shore inhabitants, and kelp, the sturdiest of all the North Sea algae, can be found at the water's edge.

ROCKY CLIFFS

Submarine cliffs are well known for their colourful fields of anemones. Hanging ledges bristle with starfishes and are home to squat lobsters, gobies, blennies and various nudibranchs. As you travel deeper, you will notice a distinct zonation of marine life, with algae, anemones, soft corals and other sedentary creatures. It is more the nature of the habitat that is appealing to scuba divers, as there are often caves and caverns associated with these cliff faces: when combined with a deep vertical wall, they undoubtedly increase the enjoyment of a dive.

FJORDS

Fjords and fjards are a typical feature of the Norwegian coastline. They are usually very deep inlets that are an extension of the precipitous cliffs that plunge into the sea. In northern regions, small offshore islands protect the inlets from the worst of the winter storms and they are incredibly scenic, with masses of marine life. Orcas that feed on the migrating shoals of herring are common in several areas, and the walls of the underwater cliffs are a diver's delight.

The Brown Swimming Crab is a North Sea species.

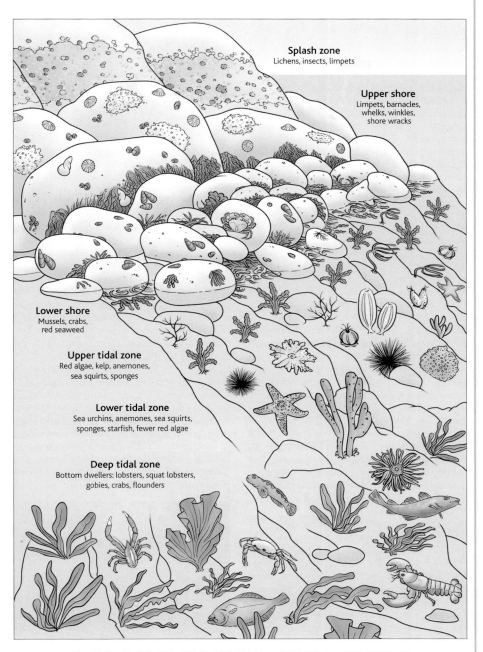

Splash zone
Lichens, insects, limpets

Upper shore
Limpets, barnacles,
whelks, winkles,
shore wracks

Lower shore
Mussels, crabs,
red seaweed

Upper tidal zone
Red algae, kelp, anemones,
sea squirts, sponges

Lower tidal zone
Sea urchins, anemones, sea squirts,
sponges, starfish, fewer red algae

Deep tidal zone
Bottom dwellers: lobsters, squat lobsters,
gobies, crabs, flounders

ZONATION OF ANIMALS AND PLANTS ON A MODERATELY EXPOSED COASTLINE

CAVES & CAVERNS

Wherever the coastline is made up of a mixture of ancient limestone or sandstone, and where geological upheaval has shifted the earth's rock strata, caves and caverns are found. One of the best known of these sites in the British Isles is Cathedral Rock near the incredibly scenic fishing harbour of St Abbs on the Berwickshire coast. A huge natural arch with a smaller 'keyhole' above is smothered in orange and white dwarf Plumose Anemones. Squat lobsters, Edible Crabs, Ballan Wrasse and at least twenty species of nudibranch can be found daily at this site, making it one of the most popular shore dives in northern Europe.

SHIPWRECKS

Attractive in their own right, shipwrecks are also important habitats, quite often found in areas that would otherwise be rather poor in marine life. Wrecks provide an important hold-fast for soft corals, anemones, sponges, sea squirts, hydroids and algae. They are also home to a number of commercial fish species, and are a natural draw for both fishermen and scuba divers. Many wrecks are, however, in deep water and quite often in areas of strong tidal currents. This limits the diver intrusion (which I personally feel is a good thing), and allows a greater degree of marine life colonization. On the other hand, of course, there are the historic wreck areas such as Scapa Flow in the Orkney Islands, the scuttled German High Seas Battle Fleet and many 'blockships' sunk deliberately by the British Admiralty, which are both a haven for marine life and quite possibly the top wreck dives in northern Europe.

OIL- & GAS-RIG SUPPORT LEGS

In the deeper regions of the North Sea, principally between northern Scotland and Norway, huge oil and gas rigs are tapping into the ancient oil and gas deposits laid down millions of years ago when the North Sea was still a tropical swamp. The steel supporting lags, lattice structures, pipelines and mooring platforms have been colonized over the years. In some instances, the marine growth is so great that the legs have to be cleaned periodically. However, they give an almost perfect zonation profile, with barnacles and mussels in the shallows,

ranging down through various algae to soft corals, sea fans and anemones. Large schools of fish are found here, and many use the rig supports as shelter and as hatcheries. The rigs also attract larger species of fish such as Conger Eels by the score and even Porbeagle Sharks.

PIERS

The most obvious of the manmade structures that abut the seashore, the piers and breakwaters found around the shores of the North Sea are the only shore access on many stretches of coastline, particularly in Denmark and Norway. Man has irrevocably changed the original coastline in pursuit of more living space, commercial enterprises and tourist facilities. The piers and breakwaters have evolved over the years as boat traffic has altered in shape, size and frequency of visits.

When all else fails and you want a reasonable dive in fair conditions with a super abundance of marine life, piers and breakwaters are the places to visit. They usually include octopus, cuttlefish, anemones, sponges, mussels and many different types of fish, as well as numerous other invertebrates that live on or in the encrusting algae.

KELP FOREST

One of the single most important habitats is the kelp forest that fringes the North Sea. There are several species of kelp, but all of them act as holdfasts for other marine organisms. Some are eaten by species such as sea urchins, and most are encrusted to some level by hydroids, sea mats, sea squirts and different species of shrimp and nudibranch.

The top of a kelp forest.

SAND

Wind-blown sand on both sides of the North Sea has created huge sand dunes and even islands made only of sand particles. Held together by hardy grasses, some sand dunes grow in height yearly, while others are constantly being eroded by rising tides and shifting currents.

Typically, worm castes of marine worms are seen in most sandy places (usually even at low tide). The tracks of marine snails and other creatures are also found, and this habitat is home to flounders, skates, rays, scallops and other diurnal and nocturnal animals. Many burrowing animals make sand their home, including starfishes, urchins, Masked Crabs, shells, anemones, eels and various types of fish.

MUD

Deeper seabeds and those affected by river run-off build up muddy layers due to the amount of detritus that gets washed into them during periodic winter storms and heavy rainfall. Burrowing animals such as various molluscs, sea pens, mud crabs, brittlestars, burrowing anemones, flatfishes and Langoustine are typical of this habitat, and are all excellent photographic subjects.

TIDAL ESTUARIES

While tidal estuaries are not exactly easy to explore due to their remoteness and vulnerability to storms and flooding, they are a very import ecosystem. Literally millions of seabirds rest or feed in these areas because of the high level of nutrients and marine life to be found in them. Over 6,000 breeding Common Seals live in the Wash region of south-east England, and Grey Seals can be found in the Farne Islands, Orkney, Denmark and Norway.

TIDAL RAPIDS

Common in a number of localities between various islands, tidal rapids are home to algae, sponges, tube worms, anemones, soft corals and other invertebrates that feed on the fast-moving plankton passing on their way four times each day. Here the generally scoured, rocky seabed is a mass of life.

THE WATER COLUMN & PLANKTON

The waters of the North Sea are largely influenced by the waters of the north-east Atlantic. Surface currents moving at approximately 2½km (1½ miles) per day sweep relatively warm water northwards and around the west coast of Scotland, then through the Pentland Firth (between the Orkney Islands and mainland Scotland), and southwards along the east coast of Scotland.

From here the water mixes with the column of the North Sea water (the movement of which is variable and wind-driven) and south-flowing, colder water from Shetland, northern Norway and the Arctic.

Plankton (both phytoplankton and zooplankton) fulfils a fundamental role in the food chain of pelagic (oceanic) wildlife. The abundance of plankton is strongly influenced by factors such as depth, tidal mixing and temperature stratification, all of which determine the vertical stability of the water column.

The distribution of planktonic species is influenced directly by salinity and temperature, by water flows in the area and by the presence of local seabed communities.

Plankton blooms begin well offshore in March, when nutrient levels are high, when the amount of daylight increases and when the sea water gradually warms. Within the North Sea area, blooms are dominated by diatoms, which spread westwards throughout the North Sea by April. After the diatom peak, dinoflagellates *Ceratium lineatum* and *Dinophysis norvegica* become predominant during the summer in areas near the shore.

Diatoms tend to predominate in inshore mixed waters, while dinoflagellates are more often found in stratified offshore waters during the summer and autumn.

The waters of the North Sea support important commercial fisheries, with several species of fish feeding directly on plankton. Plankton also has a fundamental role in the food chain of many species of benthic and pelagic wildlife, including jellyfishes and non-exploited fishes such as the Basking Shark.

MARINE CONSERVATION IN THE NORTH SEA

There are still surprisingly few conservation zones within the confines of the North Sea, but governments are now waking up to the necessity of marine conservation, not only to protect the dwindling fish stocks, but also to legislate for effluent discharge, coastal development, tourism facilities, and wind and water power turbines.

In fact, every aspect of the sea and its impact on humans has to be re-examined very closely to protect us and the environment for the future. Sadly, there is very little protective legislation for the North Sea in the British Isles, although other bordering countries have been much more proactive in this regard.

An area of only approximately 2,700sq km of Norway's marine waters is currently designated as protected under the Nature Conservation Act. Norway has an international responsibility to safeguard a representative selection of fjord and coastal area types that are not found anywhere else in the world. None of the national parks includes the skerries off the coast, and fjords are very poorly represented.

Protected areas in Svalbard were originally established under the 1925 Svalbard Act. When the Svalbard Environmental Protection Act entered into force on 1 July 2002, the existing protection orders were amended somewhat. All national parks and nature reserves in Svalbard are now protected under the new act. In all, 65 per cent of the area of the islands is protected, together with approximately 75 per cent of the territorial waters out to the 12 nautical mile territorial limit. The newest national park, Indre Wijdefjorden, was established in 2005.

In Denmark, there has been a national call to ban fishing for cod to allow the stocks to replenish themselves, and about 19 per cent of the Baltic is currently declared as marine protected; realistically, however, only 1 per cent is protected under a national park basis. Most of the protected areas are in southern Sweden, Finland, Estonia, Latvia, Poland, Germany and Denmark.

The coast of Germany on either side of Denmark has a number of protected areas, including the Nationalpark Niedersachsisches Wattenmeer, Nationalpark Hamburgisches Wattenmeer, Nationalpark Holsteinisches Wattenmeer, Nationalpark Vorpommersche Baddenlandschaft and, north of Rugen Island, the Nationalpark Jasmund.

In the Netherlands there are two large protected areas: in the north there is the Schiermonnikoog National Park and in the south the Zuid-Kennerland National Park.

There are very few totally protected areas along the east coast of the United Kingdom, but there are Special Areas of Conservation in the Wash, the Humber Estuary and the North Northumberland and Berwickshire Coast Special Area of Conservation. One particular success story is particularly worthy of inclusion, and is described opposite.

MAKING CHOICES IN MARINE CONSERVATION

- When booking a diving holiday, research the area first and use only diving schools that are involved with their local marine parks and conservation initiatives.
- Contact the appropriate conservation agencies to see if there is specific information on the areas that you want to visit and perhaps dive in.
- If you are using a tour operator, ask if the company has an environmental policy and whether it contributes to marine conservation societies.
- Make sure that dive shops and operators explain their specific conservation policies before a dive or snorkel trip, as this will undoubtedly help your awareness and lessen your impact on the marine environment. You may find that there is a particular project that you can become involved with, for example one with the Marine Conservation Society.
- Follow the example of other conservationists and use biodegradable shampoos, dispose of your litter appropriately, recycle wherever you can, use fresh water very sparingly, become actively involved in seabed and beach clean-up campaigns and, wherever you are able to do so, further the conservation message.

ST ABBS & EYEMOUTH VOLUNTARY MARINE NATURE RESERVE

Marine Conservation has been important around St Abbs and Eyemouth on the south-east coast of Scotland since a voluntary ban on the removal of shellfish was first imposed by divers back in the early 1970s, with many diving clubs supporting this move. The first real change came in 1978, when the author of this book declared a small area to the north of Eyemouth the first voluntary marine reserve in Scotland. Barefoots, as it was then known, is still an integral part of the St Abbs and Eyemouth Voluntary Marine Nature Reserve, which was founded in 1984 and officially opened by Professor David Bellamy in 1986. Located just 11km (7 miles) north of the English Border, the reserve now extends from the Hurkar Rocks at Eyemouth to St Abbs Head. It includes 7km (4.35 miles) of coastline and out to the 50m (165ft) depth contour. This area has since been upgraded to a Static Gear fishing preserve and is now part of the North Northumberland and Berwickshire Coast Special Area of Conservation, which is effectively the largest marine conservation area in Europe.

Since 1986, the marine reserve has been able to employ a warden who has liaised with divers, school groups, conservation organizations and local council authorities. Publicity materials have been published, the rockpool rambles are particularly well attended and a new code of conduct has been produced for the benefit of all visitors to the area. The marine reserve has 17 member partners on the committee, including local council authorities, diving clubs, fishermen and conservation groups.

The rugged shoreline is home to some of the greatest diversity of marine life to be found around the entire British coast. Tidal currents from both the warm North Atlantic Drift and the much colder Arctic Tidal Stream terminate along this stretch of coastline. They have created an area of clear, clean water unrivalled in the North Sea, where cold-water species live alongside more exotic warm-water species.

There is an almost total lack of 'diver pollution', apart from at one or two of the most popular sites during peak holiday time. This is due to the infrastructure available, such as good road and rail links, accommodation of various types and standards, equipment sales and hire, boat hire, launching facilities, compressors, wrecks, good photography, and so on. The dives within the confines of the marine reserve range from easy, gently sloping shore dives to challenging drift dives in difficult tidal conditions.

The seabed is generally covered with large boulders falling away to gravel and sand at about the 20m (66ft) zone. The exposed cliff faces are renowned for the great diversity of marine life they support and are festooned with Dead Man's Fingers, brilliantly coloured anemones, hydroids, tunicates, fishes and crustaceans. On these cliffs, Ballan Wrasse eat out of your hand, and wolf fishes try to eat your hand itself! The predominant feature is the kelp forest that fringes much of the coast, grazed by sea urchins and home to spider crabs, nudibranchs and Two-spot Blennies. Further offshore are brittlestar beds with Giant Dahlia and Plumose Anemones, the rare Arctic Anemone, burrowing anemones and huge angler fishes. Octopus and squid are common on night dives, and the rare Yarrel's Blenny is not rare here among the gullies, canyons and caves that cut through the headlands.

Continuing work within the reserve includes water-temperature and clarity readings, marine-life surveys and the maintenance of an important educational role. The European Union has recognized the significant part that the reserve has played in education and conservation, and the entire area is now designated as a Special Area of Conservation. This is still the only marine reserve in Scotland and it has long been established as the ideal site for all standards of diver. The reserve is so rich in marine habitats and wildlife that it is regarded as one of the best shore-diving locations in the British Isles, and it is in the top ten regions for rockpools in northern Europe. Contact www.marine-reserve.co.uk for further information.

CODE OF CONDUCT FOR VISITORS TO MARINE SITES

General
Make sure you are safe Be suitably equipped; be aware of tides, currents and weather conditions; take care near cliffs; dive boats should fly the A flag when divers are down.
Respect the interests of wildlife and other people Avoid disturbing wildlife; respect the privacy and livelihoods of those who live by the sea; park with others in mind; obey local regulations – for instance, follow the harbour master's instructions at harbours.
Leave the area as you found it Take your litter home – it is unsightly and can be hazardous to marine life; keep your dog (if you have one) from fouling beaches and other areas on land; take photos, not living animals; follow the specific points below.

Divers
• Leave animals and plants where you find them and take care not to damage them.
• Do not tamper with lobster pots – it is illegal and dangerous to do so.
• Control your buoyancy and do not use spear guns or hooks.
• Take your litter home with you and do not pollute the sea.
• Avoid losing fishing tackle by using gear suitable for the ground and an appropriate rig design.
• Keep your distance from seabirds, seals and dolphins to avoid disturbing them.
• Look out for your safety at all times, check the tides and keep back from cliff edges.

Anglers
• Obey local angling regulations.
• Bring all bait with you – do not collect it from the shore.
• Hang on to your tackle, use gear suitable for the ground you are fishing on and design your rig appropriately. Lost hooks and lines cost you money, and can foul props as well as harm wildlife – and other beach users.

Boat Users
• Reduce speed (to below 6 knots) when close to cliffs, and do not scare nesting birds off eggs or disturb chicks.
• If you come across dolphins or other large animals, maintain a steady speed and parallel course. Do not move across their path or chase them.
• Take care with paints, chemicals, waste oil and spare line, and do not let them get into the sea.

Rockpoolers
• Animals and seaweeds removed from rocks or kept in buckets for a long time will die, so avoid removing them from their habitats.
• If you must handle any animals you find, do so with care and put them back where you found them.
• If you lift rocks, do so carefully and put them back just as they were.

Walkers
• Avoid disturbing coastal birds and animals. Do not get too close to them – use binoculars to get a better view.
• Take extra care during sensitive times of the year in places where animals may be feeding, resting, breeding or with their young.
• Keep your dog (if you have one) under control.

CLASSIFICATION & NOMENCLATURE

Most species names in this guidebook are given in both the common and Latin scientific formats. Common names are given wherever possible, but because there are many different countries and languages situated around the borders of the North Sea, it is virtually impossible to find common-name descriptions to suit all species.

The scientific name describing the nomenclature of a particular animal is very important. In various parts of the world, or even in the same region, you may come across several common names for the same creature. This can be confusing. When identifying or describing a particular animal, it is therefore preferable to use its scientific name, which changes rarely (if at all) and is the name that is used internationally. This helps to avoid confusion as to its identity.

The correct naming of a species is important for your own logbook records and essential to scientists and marine biologists studying flora and fauna now and in the future.

The modern binomial system of nomenclature (which includes the genus and species names) was developed by a Swede called Carolus Linnaeus and dates from publications of his *Systema Natura* in 1735 and subsequent years.

The scientific (Latin) name of an animal includes the name of the genus to which it belongs, which is written in italics, or even underlined in some texts. This first name always starts with a capital letter, and is followed by the species name, which is always spelt with a small letter, e.g. *Carcinus maenus* (Shore Crab). This particular crab is also known by the common names Green Crab, Harbour Crab, Parten and other variations – hence the importance of the scientific name.

Once you get into the habit of using the proper scientific names, you will find it easy and useful to describe species in a common language understood by both the scientific community and enthusiastic amateurs.

THE ANIMAL GROUPS

The marine life to be found in the North Sea is as diverse as the habitats that it lives in.

MAMMALS

The most common of all the animal groups are the seals, with several thousand Grey and Common Seals to be found around the shores, particularly from the Wash to the Orkney Islands in the British Isles.

Cetaceans are always a delight to see, and sightings of Common Dolphins and porpoises are regular. Baleen Whales, Fin Whales and Sperm Whales are also encountered, as are Orcas in northern Norway, where they hunt migrating shoals of herring.

Otters are also users of the sea and they hunt in a number of locations along the shoreline and deeper rockpools, where they catch eelpout and lumpsuckers.

The Grey Seal – one of two North Sea seal species.

SEABIRDS

While seabirds can hardly be described as marine inhabitants, the species around the shores of the North Sea most certainly depend on the abundance of the sea for their very life and, in some instances, through man's fault, also their death from oil spills and other such calamities.

Huge numbers of breeding seabirds inhabit the coasts of the North Sea, whether just briefly during the mating season, during migration or seasonally, as in the case of many seagulls and terns. In a number of diving locations, where exceptional dive sites are below nesting sites, divers are often treated to an underwater ballet as Razorbills, Guillemots and even gannets swim by.

SEAGRASSES

Surprisingly few species of true seagrass are found around the shores of the North Sea, with only three related species being evident. A true plant needs light to photosynthesize and produces both flowers and seeds – all other underwater structures that look similar are not true plants, and are more likely to be algae. Many anemones, for example, look like colourful flowers, but they are actually animals.

ALGAE

Three different colour groups of algae can be found around the shores – brown, red and green – with literally hundreds of species in each group. This guide features only some of the largest and most common species that can be seen while exploring the North Sea and its coast.

SPONGES

Sponges are an ancient group of animals. They are quite simple in structure and exist by breathing in sea water loaded with nutrient food through small holes, and expelling the clean water through a single hole or several large holes.

ANTHOZOA

This is a huge group of invertebrates that covers pretty well all the creatures with stinging cells or feeding polyps. It includes anemones, hydroids, corals and jellyfishes, with a few other relatives in between.

ARTHROPODS

Arthropods are another huge family with virtually all its members being marine, except for a few critters that hop about on the seashore. This group includes the crustaceans such as sea spiders, other insects, various crabs, shrimps and lobsters.

ECHINODERMS

This is quite a complex group of creatures whose habitat is marine, although a few species, such as sea urchins and starfishes, often get stranded at low tide. It includes starfishes, sea urchins, brittlestars, crinoids and sea cucumbers.

MOLLUSCS

In this large family you can find nudibranchs or sea slugs, flat worms, snails, bivalves (such as oysters and scallops), octopus, squid and cuttlefish.

TUNICATES

Tunicates or sea squirts look relatively inactive and generally similar. They feed on plankton, using one of two openings in their body cavity to take in food and water and the other to expel waste and water. They are hermaphroditic, and keep their eggs inside their body until they hatch. Adults may develop a thick covering, or tunic, which protects their bodies from enemies.

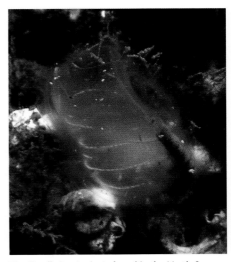

The Corella is a tunicate found in the North Sea.

EXTERNAL FEATURES OF FISHES

This diagram illustrates the main structures of a fish referred to in the species descriptions.

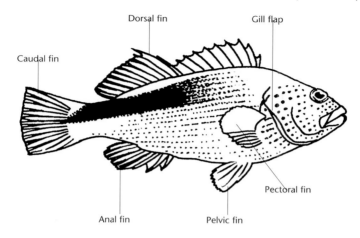

FISH IDENTIFICATION GROUPS & PICTORIAL GUIDE TO FAMILIES

Colour varies greatly between fish species, so it would seem an ideal means of identification. However, even within species, colour varies according to sex, age, region, season and surroundings. For this reason, body shape is a much more reliable means of identification. The following outlines represent the main types of fish likely to be encountered in the North Sea. Those sharing similar characteristics are grouped together for initial identification.

RAYS & SHARKS

Basking Shark, page 102

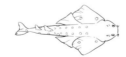

Angel Shark, page 102

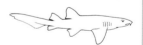

Dogfish, Spurdog and Nursehound, page 102

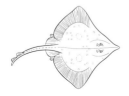

Skate, page 104

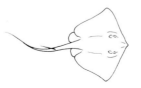

Stingray, page 104

REGULAR-SHAPED FISHES CLOSE TO OR ABOVE THE SEABED

Codfishes (Rockling), page 114

Pollack and Saithe, page 114

Wrasses, page 118

Sea Bass, page 116

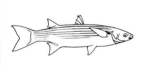

Grey Mullet, page 116

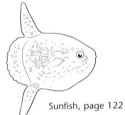

Sunfish, page 122

Salmon and Sea Trout, page 104

FISHES CLOSE TO OR ON THE SEABED

Conger Eel, page 104

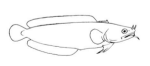

Codfishes and Ling, page 114

Red Mullet, page 116

Lumpsucker, page 112

Wolf Fish, page 122

FISHES CLOSE TO OR ON THE SEABED

Weaverfishes, page 116

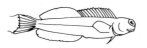

Blennies, pages 120–1

Gobies, page 120

Combers, page 116

Dragonet, page 112

IRREGULARLY SHAPED FISHES

Anglerfishes, page 110

Pipefishes, page 106

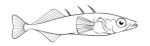

Sticklebacks, page 106

Scorpionfishes, page 110

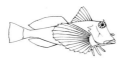

Gurnards, page 106

Flounder and Turbot, page 108

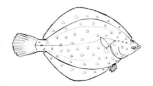

Plaice, page 108

Clingfishes, page 112

SEAGRASSES

Seagrasses are the only flowering plants in the sea and three closely related species are found in northern European waters and the countries that fringe the North Sea. Their locations are rather sporadic, but once established they can cover quite wide areas, anchoring the softer substrates of the seabed.

1 EELGRASS
Zostera marina
The flat, dark or grass-green leaves of the Eelgrass are up to 1m (3ft) long, and the plant is found on the lower shore in sheltered bays and estuaries, where it grows on sand, mud or gravel. It provides a useful home for fishes to lay eggs around, and the leaves are often colonized by small anemones and shrimps. There are two other very similar and closely related species. The Eelgrass is found throughout the North Sea region.

ALGAE

Algae are incredibly widespread and diverse, with several hundred species being recorded in the North Sea, and more being discovered each year due to invasive species being dumped into coastal waters by tankers emptying their ballast tanks, or to gradual migration from the Mediterranean and Atlantic. Some are single celled, living in the tissue of hard coral polyps, while others are multicellular, spreading over rocky surfaces. Many grow in tufts and some are so delicate that it is hard to image that they are even algae. Most species have specific predators, such as fishes, sea urchins and snails, while others form the habitat home for encrusting bryozoans, hydroids and other algae. Algae can be split into three groups, depending on their colour pigmentation – green, red and brown.

GREEN ALGAE

2 *Enteromorpha intestinalis*
The bright, light green fronds of this alga are hollow and cylindrical, and are found on all rocky shores throughout the region. It grows on rock, on large boulders and in rockpools, and can live in brackish water but tends to favour a fully marine habitat. A widespread and prolific, delicate alga, it can be found from the Arctic to the Mediterranean and even in the Pacific.

3 SEA LETTUCE or GREEN LAVER
Ulva lactuca
This is a very delicate alga, which is irregularly shaped and a brilliant light green in colour. It is easily broken and the wide-fronded leaves are often split. It enjoys a wide habitat down to as far as 18m (60ft). Tolerating reduced salinity, it appears to favour high levels of sewerage and may grow larger under such conditions.

4 PURSE CODIUM
Codium bursa
Rounded in shape and of various shades of green, this alga can grow to up to 30cm (1ft) in diameter. More common in the Mediterranean than in the North Sea, it is gradually spreading northwards and is found along the coasts of northern France and Belgium, as well as the Channel Islands and the southern coasts of England and Ireland.

5 BOOTLACE WEED, SEA LACE or CAT GUT
Chorda filum
The Bootlace Weed is long and slender, olive-green to brown in colour and unbranched. In sheltered coastal areas it can grow to as long as 6m (20ft), yet stays a slender and cylindrical shape at only about 5mm (.2in) in diameter. It forms large, entangled masses. It is a summer seasonal alga, dying off in the winter months.

1 Eelgrass

2 *Enteromorpha intestinalis*

3 Sea Lettuce

4 Purse Codium

5 Bootlace Weed

1 **THONG WEED**
Himanthalia elongate
The Thong Weed is very similar in appearance to the Bootlace Weed, *Chorda filum*. The stype or stalk is formed from a disc-like holdfast or stalked button, and the frond is broader in appearance with numerous branches. It is usually greenish-brown in colour and forms dense mats on the shoreline around deeper rockpools.

2 **SEA OAK** or **POD WEED**
Halydris siliquosa
This alga's holdfast is a flattened cone and the fronds branch alternately. A rich olive-green in colour, it has tiny air bladders that resemble seed pods (hence its name). It has a very bush-like appearance and tends to be found in the 9–15m (30–50ft) littoral zone, attached to bedrock on a gravel bottom. This is a perennial species and quite often looks decidedly untidy, but it is home to a large number of isopods and shrimps, all of which like the cover it provides.

BROWN ALGAE

There is a huge and diverse number of species of brown algae, and this group also includes the kelps and wracks (even though they look green). As a rule, brown algae are either olive-green in colour, or any shade of brown between golden to very dark.

3 **BRANCHING BROWN ALGA**
Dictyota dichotoma
This is a common alga in which the green chlorophyll is masked by brown pigments, sometimes tinging the tips a brilliant blue. It usually grows to about 15cm (6in) high with obvious dichotomously branching, ribbon-like fronds. There is no midrib to support the alga and it wafts in whatever current passes over it. It is quite fragile and is often found washed up on the shore.

4 **BROWN MANE**
Dictyosiphon spp.
There are three species of *Dictyosiphon* and they are almost impossible to tell apart. They are many-branched species, often overgrown with hydroids and bryozoans, and most commonly golden-brown in colour. They can grow to over 70cm (2ft) long, and when clumped together in large aggregations and moving in a current tend to look like a horse's mane.

KELP
There are about 30 genera of kelp worldwide. They grow in 'forests', in clear, well-aerated, clean water, and require nutrient-rich water below about 20°C (68°F). Kelp is an important canopy-forming alga that becomes home to many species and food for numerous others. It is known for its high growth rate, and a couple of species can actually grow as fast as 150cm (1½ft) per day.

During the 19th century, the word 'kelp' was closely associated with seaweeds that could be burned to obtain soda ash (primarily sodium carbonate). The seaweeds that included species from the orders of Laminariales and Fucales. While we refer to these large species collectively as 'kelp', technically the word 'kelp' derives from the name used directly to refer to their processed ashes. Kelp is harvested to be processed for alginate for thickening products such as ice cream, jelly, salad dressing and toothpaste, as well as in manufactured goods. Giant kelp is harvested almost daily in California due to its massive growth rate. Kelp is still harvested for fertilizer in the Channel Islands, Ireland, northern Scotland and Scandinavia. It is known as 'vraic' in the Channel Islands.

5 **TANGLE** or **KELP**
Laminaria digitata
This alga has a smooth-surfaced, flexible stype that is oval in cross-section. Its holdfast is quite small and intertwined, and subsequently it is often ripped up and deposited on beaches during winter storms. It can grow to up to 150cm (5ft) long, and has a large, broad frond or blade that is deeply divided into large, dark, olive-green strap-like blades. It is an important canopy-forming alga and is found from the extreme low-water zone down to around 6m (20ft). While the stype is generally clean of other organisms, the complex holdfast is usually home to a number of different species including small crabs and hydroids.

1 Thong Weed

2 Sea Oak

3 Branching Brown Alga

4 Brown Mane

5 Tangle (*right*)

1 HAIRY KELP or CUVIE
Laminaria hyperborea
This species is very similar to the Tangle, *L. digitata*, but the stype is more cylindrical in shape and has a very rough surface. As a consequence, it is usually encrusted in all manner of other marine organisms, including algae of the same and other species. The stype is twice as broad at the base, and the fronds are usually about the same length as the stype; they resemble those of the Tangle as they are also strap-like. Like the Tangle, this is a very important canopy alga that is rarely seen even at the lowest of tides, but it can grow as deep as 30m (100ft), depending on the clarity of the water column. Because the stypes of the Hairy Kelp are much stronger on this species, they tend to 'stick up' at low tide, whereas the stypes of the Tangle hang down.

2 SEA BELT, POOR MAN'S WEATHER GLASS, SUGAR KELP or OAR WEED
Laminaria saccharina
The Sea Belt has a very broad holdfast or root with quite a short stype that broadens out to a long, olive-green to brown, ribbon-like, wrinkly blade. The central rib is very much lighter in colour and is more of a pale yellow-green. It is not very strong and is quite soft and slimy to the touch. The Sea Belt is usually seen at extreme low tide, and may often be found draped across rockpools. When dry, it is favoured by a number of animals, including horses and sheep.

3 FURBELLOWS
Laminaria polyschides
The Furbellows is the largest of the European seaweeds and as it reaches maturity, the holdfast becomes large, distended and cylindrical in shape, with numerous knobbly protrusions or tubercles. The stype is cylindrical and flattened, and gradually broadens out to strap-like fronds that can be two or three times longer than the stype. This species is most common on exposed shores, and while it is known to occur in all regions of the North Sea, it is usually found in the extreme south and north, with very occasional sightings along the British east coast.

4 RIB WEED, RIBBED KELP, BLADDERLOCKS, DABBERLOCKS or MURLIN
Alaria esculenta
The Rib Weed has a strong, branching holdfast and a strong, broadleaf-like frond with a lighter coloured central line. It is incredibly strong and appears to enjoy exposed shorelines, where it is usually seen at extreme low tide. It grows higher up the littoral zone than other kelp and is most often found in deeper rockpools, or even attached to other kelp species.

WRACKS
Wracks are commonly found around all of Britain's shoreline and are the dominant species of the shallow-water algae. They are incredibly hardy and can tolerate differences in salinity and exposure to strong sunlight. Quite often they can be almost dried out on the shoreline, occurring high up the beach line, but they always revive with the incoming tide. Although these algae are included in the 'brown' group, they are in fact usually dark green in colour.

5 KNOTTED WRACK
Ascophyllum nodosum
One of the longest-growing wracks, reaching as much as 3m (10ft) in length, this is usually very dark green in colour, and dries to almost black in appearance. Every few centimetres the frond enlarges to form a cylindrical air bladder that keeps the alga afloat as the tide rises. Generally found further down the shore, this alga is often further colonized by other types of encrusting alga. It occurs on solid rock, gets battered in storms and is rather untidy in appearance.

6 HORNED WRACK
Fucus ceranoides
The stype of the Horned Wrack grows from quite a small holdfast and gradually branches as it grows. Each branch then splits, making for a fork-like appearance, but the edges of the wrack are smooth and fan-like. It closely resembles the Spiral Wrack, *F. spiralis*, but lacks the spiral formation or inflated water bladders and is more commonly found at the mouths of river estuaries or harbours, where it appears to enjoy the reduced salinity.

1 Hairy Kelp (*left*)
2 Sea Belt (*above*)

3 Furbellows (*above*)
4 Rib Weed (*left*)

5 Knotted Wrack

6 Horned Wrack

1 **TOOTHED, SERRATED** or **SAW WRACK**
Fucus serratus
This wrack is very abundant and can be found from the Baltic Sea all the way north to Iceland and as far south as Portugal. The fronds have a distinct midrib and their margins have serrated or toothed edges. The species is located quite high up the intertidal zone and can grow to up to 60cm (2ft) in length. It is often covered with tiny white hairs. Small shells often feed on this bladderless wrack.

2 **SPIRAL** or **TWISTED WRACK**
Fucus spiralis
This wrack is an intertidal, brown seaweed with a rather shortened stype and a frond that soon branches out in a twisted formation. Although it has no air bladders, it actually gives the appearance of having them, as the lobed ends are filled with water. Each frond has a characteristic ridge along the edge of the receptacles. The Spiral Wrack is found high up on the intertidal shore, usually in dense clumps, and is grazed by periwinkles. It can grow to about 40cm (16in) in length and lives to around four years old – it manages to survive even after it is extensively desiccated.

3 **BLADDER WRACK**
Fucus vesiculosus
One of the most common wracks found on the shore, the Bladder Wrack has quite a short stype and branching, ribbed fronds. The edges of the fronds are not ribbed, and air bladders are located on either side of the midrib. The plants are olive-green/brown in colour, and are a favourite of colourful periwinkles. The Bladder Wrack is harvested and fed to pigs in some areas of Scotland and Scandinavia. It is one of the most important of the wrack family and many scientific tests have been carried out on it all around the world. It has anti-coagulant and antioxidant properties, and appears to inhibit the growth of cancer cells. It also has antibacterial and antifungal properties, and is being associated with links for weight loss and the prevention of thyroid disease.

RED ALGAE

The red algae (Rhodophyta) are a very large group containing about 5,000–6,000 species worldwide. They are mainly multicellular, marine algae, and include most of the coralline algae, which secrete calcium carbonate – this plays a major role in the building of coral reefs. Red algae such as the Dulse (*Palmaria palmata*) are a traditional part of European cuisine, and algae are collected commercially for use in other products such as agar and other food additives. Red algae are most commonly found on the lower shore and shallow waters of the littoral zone. They are usually quite clean of encrusting species, but they do have a tendency to encrust other types of alga.

4 **CARRAGHEEN** or **IRISH MOSS**
Chondrus crispus
This red alga has a small, disc-like holdfast rising to a flattened stem that gradually becomes fan-like in structure. Typically, it is red to purple in colour and brightly iridescent. This small seaweed is widely distributed in Iceland, all around the British Isles, Ireland (where it is harvested as a local delicacy), Scandinavia and the Baltic.

5 **RED RAGS**
Dilsea carnosa
A common alga that is found sub-tidally, the Red Rags consists of several large, tough blades about 15cm (6in) long and usually split at the ends. They have a short stem. The Red Rags is frequently confused with *Palmaria palmata* and is also called Dulse, but unlike the Dulse it is not edible.

6 **DULSE** or **CRANNACH**
Palmaria palmata
The Dulse is a rather tough, yet raggedy red alga with a broad, flattened frond growing to about 75cm (2ft 5.5in) long and 9cm (3.5in) wide. Older, damaged fronds tend to have small branchlets growing off them. The species is found in the middle to lower shore around all areas of the North Sea. It is edible, raw or cooked, and is grazed upon by sheep and pigs.

1 Toothed Wrack

2 Spiral Wrack

3 Bladder Wrack

4 Carragheen

5 Red Rags

6 Dulse

1 JANIA
Jania rubens

Similar in structure to *Corallina* species, but much paler and thinner, the Jania comprises a large clump of calcareous and jointed fronds that branch off dichotomously. The reproductive organs are in the form of a swelling at the joints and difficult to see. Growing from 1.5 to 4cm (½–1½in) in diameter, this rosy red alga forms circular clumps in shallow water and is quite often associated with numerous other algae that it tends to colonize.

2 SEA BEECH
Delesseria sanguinea

This is a common algae that is usually found on large boulders, but more commonly grows on the stypes of the Hairy Kelp, *Laminaria hyperborea*. The frond is leaf-like and has a distinct midrib with veins paired laterally, giving it a rather ruffled margin. It is deep red in colour and quite fragile, but will grow to about 30cm (11.8in) in length. The blades are oval and leaf-like, and reminiscent of beech leaves (hence the common name of the species). Each leaf has a wavy margin and is supported by a conspicuous midrib with opposite pairs of lateral veins. The stype is short and cylindrical, and only about 1cm (.39in) long. It hardly ever branches, which allows the leaf-like blades to grow singularly. Reproduction takes place in October, but the fertilized eggs are not released into the open water until February. When the leaves of the Sea Beech become battered by winter storms, it is difficult to make a correct identification of the species.

3 MEMBRANOPTERA
Membranoptera alata

This species of red alga is found throughout the North Sea and into southern Scandinavia. It grows to about 15cm (6in) tall and has a distinct midrib, but the branches lack veins. The midrib is usually green, and the fronds are dark red and usually flat and narrow, with many fine lateral veins. It has many branches that rise from a central axis. This alga is an epiphyte, and is usually found attached to laminarians. It also inhabits deeper, shaded rockpools, and is perennial.

4 ENCRUSTING ALGA
Lithophyllum incrustans

This is an encrusting alga that is roughly circular in shape and grows in overlapping pads that are light purple in colour fading to paler at the margins. Growing to up to 10cm (3.9in) in diameter, the alga often degenerates and regenerates, so the thickness tends to vary. It is found on the shoreline and can encrust seemingly quite large expanses of bare rock, but can be found as deep as 9m (30ft).

5 CORALLINA
Corallina officinalis

The Corallina is a curious alga that has a hard, calcareous crust. The fronds are slightly cylindrical and jointed, and become more and more compressed towards the tips of the alga. It is typically a dull, light purple in colour, and the branches are quite stiff when erect. It appears to favour moderate to heavy wave action, and is grazed upon by several species of nudibranch, including *Doto* spp.

6 MAERLE or SCOTTISH CORAL
Phymatolithon calcareum

The most curious of all the calcareous algae, the Maerle can usually be seen on coarse sand down to depths of 18m (60ft). It forms loose beds of hard, disjointed branches that interconnect, forming a firm substrate. Pale purple in colour while alive, it breaks up and bleaches white when dead and can form hard ridges in the sandy furrows on the seabed. Each segment may only be around 13–30mm (½–11.8in) in size, but it will have several joints and resembles the bryozoan *Pentapora fascialis*, which is attached, unlike the Maerle, which is loose. Maerle beds are home to juveniles of many creatures such as hermit crabs, feather starfishes and a number of burrowing worms. Sea cucumbers and starfishes are also found amid this crusty alga.

1 Jania

3 Membranoptera

4 Encrusting Alga

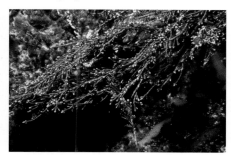

5 Corallina

2 Sea Beech

6 Maerle

SPONGES

(FAMILY PORIFERA)

Sponges are sessile animals (although some may be attached to encrusting snails and animals that give them propulsion). They are simply constructed, with a single or interlaced body cavity that has large exhalant pores called oscula, and smaller inhalant openings lined with special cells called choanocytes through which water is passed. The exhalant tube is usually located at the highest point of the animal to allow for waste water to be carried away efficiently. The hard structure of a sponge contains small calcareous or siliceous spikes or spicules that support the animal. Sponges have no internal organs, yet despite their simplicity are very successful organisms that are found worldwide in many different habitats. From an ancient class of animals, they are often difficult to identify because they change shape to suit their environment. In very exposed locations, sponges are flattened and often cover large expanses of rocky substrate. In calm, sheltered conditions, many sponges grow quite spectacularly with large, branching arms and delicate formations.

1 CLATHRINA or STRING VEST SPONGE
Clathrina coriacea
Rarely found in depths of less than 10m (33ft), this golden-yellow or white, honeycomb sponge is only 3cm (11.8in) high, but grows extensively over wide areas. The Clathrina prefers a shaded habitat and is common in caverns and under overhangs. Constructed of many small tubules that link and weave together, it forms a raised pad that quite often hangs down from a cave wall. Looking rather like a small lump of netting, the exhalant valves or oscula are found at the ends of the interlocking tubes. The Clathrina is commonly associated with the Baked Bean Ascidian, *Dendrodoa grossularia*, and the combination of the two creates a very marked appearance of red and white or red and yellow on cavern walls.

2 URN SPONGE
Sycon ciliatum
The Urn Sponge is quite distinctive and small, with a singular ovoid or spherical-shaped tube that is around 5cm (1.9in) in length and creamy-yellow in colour. It has a single, large oscula at the top surrounded by a stiff, spiky collar. Preferring shallow water and found in beds of mixed algae, this is an annual species that releases its larvae in the spring.

3 PURSE SPONGE
Scypha compressa
This sponge has a characteristic vase shape, growing to about 2cm (¾in) tall and 1cm (⅛in) wide. It has a large oscula at the top and is grey to creamy-white in colour. Although it is generally single, it will also grow in small clumps and is usually found on *Laminaria hyperborea*.

4 SUBERITES or HERMIT CRAB SPONGE
Suberites domuncula
This sponge grows on most hard surfaces, but is perhaps most commonly known to smother whelk shells that are home to hermit crabs. The whelk shell dissolves gradually and the sponge itself becomes the home of the hermit crab. It is lugged around on the crab's travels, and grows to accommodate it without it having to change shells. Generally orange in colour, it is firm and rough-surfaced to the touch.

5 SCALLOP SPONGE
Pseudosuberites sulphereus
Little is known about this sponge other than that it is predominantly found adorning the tops of Queen Scallops, *Aequipecten opercularis*, and occasionally on small stones. It forms a very thin, irregular shape, covering the scallop shell. It is pale ochre to pink in colour.

1 Clathrina

2 Urn Sponge

3 Purse Sponge

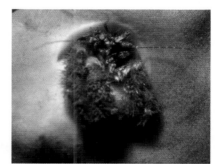

4 Suberites

5 Scallop Sponge

1 POLYMASTIA
Polymastia boletiformis
This is a relatively firm sponge, cylindrical in shape and growing to about 10cm (3.9in) in diameter. Its upper surface is covered in fairly stout tubercles, with the oscula located at the tops. It is orange to yellowish in colour, and is found throughout northern Europe.

2 CHIMNEY POLYMASTIA
Polymastia mamillaris
Although the Chimney Polymastia is a close relative of the Polymastia, *P. boletiformis*, it is more low-lying and often covered in silty sediment. Its most distinguishing feature is the number of 'chimneys' that project above it. These papillae (exhalant tubes) vary in size according to age or even habitat conditions, as they may have to project above the muddy substrate that often covers the sponge. The species is usually pale yellow or cream in colour, and will grow to over 15cm (5.9in) across.

3 YELLOW HANGING SPONGE
Halichondria bowerbanki
Found in varying shades of yellow and green, this species is probably much more common than was once thought – due to its small size it is easily overlooked by marine life observers. It looks like a normal sponge, but has long, trailing, thin extensions, and many inhalant and exhalant holes lined with calcareous spicules to trap organic matter. The sponge grows on rocks, algae holdfasts and almost anything with a hard surface, including various crabs and shells.

4 SMALL BREADCRUMB SPONGE
Adocia cineria
This sponge forms irregular, very soft clumps that often cover wide areas. It likes sub-tidal conditions, and is often exposed for a long time at low tide. The surface is rough, like breadcrumbs, and it has many raised pores. It has a huge colour range from orange to vivid green, depending on its location. It is a polymorphous sponge that has hardly any identification features, other than its ability to form large, laterally spreading, encrusting masses of interconnecting small, finger-like protrusions. This is a very soft and fragile sponge.

5 ENCRUSTING SPONGE
Myxilla incrustans
A rather untidy-looking encrusting sponge, this species can spread over wide areas. It is covered in small pits and is a bit ragged in appearance. Usually found on the lower shore or in sub-tidal regions, it prefers smooth rocks, but will also encrust the stalks of hydroids, grow around the bases of algae or even attach itself to the top carapaces of spider crabs. The Encrusting Sponge is usually found in association with other sponges.

6 SMALL VASE SPONGE
Axinella infundibuliformis
This small, cream-coloured sponge is vase or cup shaped, with a wide-opening oscula bearing a collar. It is about 2.5cm (1in) tall and may appear in small clumps. Widely distributed in the North Sea, it is usually located on an upwards-facing rock subsrate and is known from all depths. It is small in stature, but the funnel can be about 10cm (3in) in diameter, depending on the depth and tidal conditions.

7 TREE SPONGE
Raspalia ramose
As its name suggests, this sponge forms a tree-like formation with rather stout branches and a fan-like structure. Usually dark greyish-brown in colour, it may grow to up to 15cm (5.9in) tall. Its small oscula are scattered across the surface, which is hairy in appearance or even rather untidy looking. It is a northern species that is found from the Baltic all the way to Iceland and south to the Bay of Biscay, the British Isles and Ireland.

8 ORANGE MAT SPONGE
Amphilectus fucorum
The Orange Mat Sponge is quite variable in form. It often has long, thin, erect lobes, but in many areas it is characterized by its formations of thin encrusting mats that extend over wide areas. The oscula are very obvious – raised and frequently in lines – with the sponge having a general orange colour. The species is often found on kelp holdfasts, and may encrust several hydroids and even the parchment tubes of Peacock Worms, *Sabella pavonina*.

1 Polymastia

2 Chimney Polymastia

3 Yellow Hanging Sponge

4 Small Breadcrumb Sponge

5 Encrusting Sponge

6 Small Vase Sponge

7 Tree Sponge

8 Orange Mat Sponge

CNIDARIANS

This large and fundamentally simple group of animals is widely distributed and seemingly totally diverse, with such a wide array of forms that they do not appear to be obviously related to each another. The family (phylum) formerly known as Coelenterata includes true hard corals, soft corals, sea pens, sea fans, anemones, sea firs (hydroids), zoanthids and jellyfishes. Cnidarians occur in two different forms – an attached polyp or group of polyps, or a free-floating medusa.

All the species are radically symmetrical without a right or left side. They have a single body cavity and a single terminal opening, usually surrounded by one or numerous rings of tentacles. It is these tentacles in various forms and adaptations that group the family together. Each tentacle is armed with stinging cells called cnidocytes, containing nematocysts. A nematocyst consists of a small capsule that contains a smooth or barbed thread coiled inside. Used for defence or aggression and for catching prey, the stinging cells may also be found on other parts of the body. The toxins released when these 'harpoons' are fired may be powerful enough to cause a severe sting.

The typical cnidarian shape is that of the anemone type with a single mouth ringed with tentacles, with which the animal stings, stuns or captures its prey, which is drawn into the mouth and thence to the single, sac-like body cavity. Waste matter also exits through the mouth. Most cnidarians reproduce sexually, releasing floating larvae that inhabit other areas of the ocean. Some species split or bud to produce new polyps that remain attached, thereby increasing the size of the colony, while others release free-floating eggs and sperm that are fertilized in open water, producing medusa that eventually settle back onto the seabed.

HYDROIDS (SEA FIRS)

Commonly referred to as 'sea firs', hydroids usually live attached to rocky substrates or shipwrecks and have a rather complicated life history. They are often mistaken for plants and algae, and generally overlooked because they are so small. Living below the kelp line, they form delicate, fern- or feather-like groups, and can be quite profuse in certain areas. During sexual reproduction, they produce a free-swimming tiny jellyfish called a hydromedusa. Although most hydroids have tiny polyps, they pack powerful stings and contact with them should be avoided.

1 TUBULARIA or OATEN PIPE
Tubularia indivisa
This hydroid can grow to over 15cm (6in) high and has stiff, yellowish stalks that support a delicate, pink, flower-like single polyp called a hydranth, which is surrounded by two rings of tentacles. The stalks are often intertwined, making them appear more like a clump than

individual animals. Tubularia can grow in huge numbers and are grazed upon by the Grey Sea Slug, *Aeolidia papillosa*.

2 BELL HYDROID
Tubularia larynx
This species is very similar to the Tubularia, *T. indivisa*, but here the stalks are branching and the animal is slightly smaller in size and makes more obvious clumps. It also has a flower-like, single polyp on the tip of each segmented stalk (the hydranth), and is surrounded by two rings of tentacles.

3 OBELIA
Obelia geniculata
The Obelia is a very distinctive, creeping hydroid that tends to colonize the fronds of various wracks and kelp plants. The polyps grow on alternate sides of zigzag branching stems. Each polyp is held within a protective cup, and when disturbed the tentacle of the polyp can withdraw inside the cup. These pale cream hydroids grow to around 5cm (1.9in) in length.

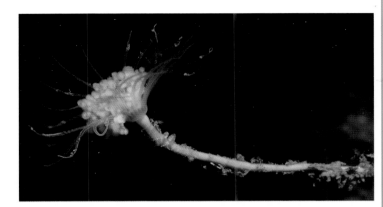

1 Tubularia (*right*)
2 Bell Hydroid
  (*below*)
3 Obelia (*bottom*)

1 HERMIT CRAB HYDROID
Hydractinia echinata
This is one of the most distinctive hydroids because it is almost entirely found only on the shell home of the Common Hermit Crab, *Pagarus bernhardus*. It gives the shell a general 'fuzzy' appearance, and actually forms a thick, horny mat that covers the entire shell. Each hydranth can grow to 13mm (.5in), and is club-shaped with an upper ring of eight long tentacles and an inner ring of eight short tentacles. The species ranges from northern Norway to north-west Africa.

2 MUSSEL HYDROID
Abietinaria abietina
A small hydroid, individual in stature but growing in colonies, this is usually attached to Common Mussels, *Mytilus edulis*. It has a pale coloration, slightly grey with white polyps growing off fairly rigid stems, and small, short branches alternating left and right up the stem. An erect species, it forms a slender, feathery shape to around 25mm (1in) high.

3 HERRINGBONE HYDROID
Halecium halecium
This hydroid has a distinct long, slender feather shape, with alternate branches extending from the main stem. It can grow to 25cm (9.8in) high and usually forms small clumps, with the branches equally spaced, alternating from left to right up the stem.

4 COARSE FEATHER HYDROID
Hydrallmania falcata
Usually pale cream or buff-coloured, the Coarse Feather Hydroid has coarse, feather-like side branches that tend to grow in a spiral fashion. Its stem is rather slender. It is a sub-tidal species usually found below 6m (20ft), and can grow to about 10–30cm (4–12in) tall. It grows in tide-swept and sand-scoured sites, usually attached to stones, rocks and wrecks. The feeding heads are arranged in clusters and curve outwards, with their aperture rim smooth. The Coarse Feather Hydroid is widely distributed throughout the North Sea.

5 SEA BEARD
Nemertesia antennina
Generally found in depths exceeding 15m (50ft), this colonial hydroid forms clumps of about 50 individuals and is approximately 15cm (6in) high. The stems are stiff and unbranched, and the polyps are attached to tiny whorled branchlets protected by a calcareous cup. The hydroid is yellowish in colour and is a favourite food species of the tiny nudibranch *Doto pinnatifida*, which also lays its whorled egg ribbons on the stalks.

6 BOTTLEBRUSH HYDROID
Thuiaria thuja
The Bottlebrush Hydroid is a northern species that occurs as far south as St Abbs in south-east Scotland and is found along the Scandinavian coastline, where it favours a relatively deep location generally below 18m (60ft) and in swift-moving water. It has a single, stiff, ribbed stalk that develops into the classic bottlebrush shape with spiraling branches that are divided many times. Pale cream in colour, the stalks and polyps of the Bottlebrush Hydroid are home to many species, including the curious crustacean Astacilla, *Astacilla longicornis* (see page 70), and various shrimps.

7 BRANCHING SEA BEARD
Nemertesia ramosa
A colonial species like other, similar members of this group, the Branching Sea Beard is very similar to the Sea Beard, *N. antennina*. In this species, however, there is a distinct single stalk that rapidly forms irregularly branched stems which divide and subdivide. The arrangement of the polyps is identical to that in *N. antennina*, where they grow out of a protective cup arranged in whorls around the stalks. The Branching Sea Beard grows to about 15cm (6in) high. It usually forms a small colony often solitary at the base, but more usually with several individuals grouped together. It is creamy-yellow in colour, and is found attached to bedrock interspaced with shelly gravel in moderate tide-swept regions. The species is preyed upon by several species of nudibranch.

1 Hermit Crab Hydroid

2 Mussel Hydroid

3 Herringbone Hydroid

4 Coarse Feather Hydroid

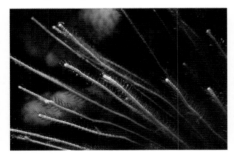

5 Sea Beard

6 Bottlebrush Hydroid

7 Branching Sea Beard

1 SQUIRREL'S TAIL
Sertullaria argenta
This is a colonial hydroid that can grow to 15cm (6in) long. It has slender stems and creeping roots and branches alternately, often with more branchlets. Its appearance is feathery, with the white polyps arranged in two rows and each polyp protected inside a small cup. It can be found attached to scallop shells and often on crabs' backs, and occurs at most water depths. It is very similar to the Whiteweed, *Sertullaria cupressina*, but can grow to 60cm (24in) and is more often found trailing over the sea floor.

2 PLUMED HYDROID
Aglophenia pluma
Colonies of the Plumed Hydroid resemble a feather with a straight stem and two series of alternating branches, and can grow to 15cm (6in) long. The species is usually pale brown or yellowish in colour, and during the summer months its egg cases are quite clearly visible on the branches of the stalks. It is unbranched, and its small hydrothecal rim is rounded, low and has ten tentacles emerging from it.

3 SEA FEATHER
Gymnangium montagui
The rather striking fronds of the Sea Feather are over 10cm (4in) tall and occur in depths of over 18m (60ft), typically on exposed cliff faces or shipwrecks, where there is plenty of aeration and passing planktonic particles. Golden brown in colour, colonies may contain several hundred fronds. This is a southerly species, also found in the Mediterranean.

JELLYFISHES & CTENOPHORES

Jellyfishes are free-floating or swimming medusa in which the polyp stage of the life cycle has either been totally suppressed or extremely reduced. The upper surface of jellyfishes is generally smooth to the touch and is known as the aboral or exumbrellar portion. The subumbrellar portion is underneath and contains the various combinations of tentacles and mouthparts, which are armed with a variety of stinging cells. Jellyfishes are quite capable of directional movement, which is achieved through pulsing the outer bell and creating a staccato propulsion. More often than not they are at the mercy of tidal movements and bad weather, and can be washed up on tourist beaches in large numbers.

Ctenophores are quite similar to jellyfishes in that they too are at the mercy of tide and current, but their movements are controlled by conscious movements of the cilia. These tiny, hair-like parts are arranged in rows called combs and they beat in waves, creating directional movement.

Ctenphores actively hunt prey and appear to be fully aware of their surroundings. Many are know to emit light at night or in the depths to attract prey species such as small shrimps or other ctenophores.

4 STALKED JELLYFISH
Haliclystus auricular
This is an unusual small, slightly bell-shaped jellyfish, which stays attached to algae in the sub-tidal zone. It is funnel-shaped and has eight small, raised clubs that are the ends of the arms, which extend to the base of the mouth. Translucent and light brownish in colour, the Stalked Jellyfish only grows to around 1cm (1⅓in) in diameter.

5 LION'S MANE JELLYFISH
Cyanea capillata
This is a huge and quite dangerous jellyfish that inhabits virtually all of the North Sea region, except the very south around France and Belgium, where the northerly currents keep it in the northern regions. It is orange to brick-red in colour, and the bell has been known to reach over 1.8m (6ft), but is more commonly around 50cm (1½ft). The margins of the bell are lobed and it has around 65 tentacles arranged in 8 groups that are attached underneath the hood, as well as 4 thick, frilled arms. The highly toxic stinging tentacles have been known to stretch to over 6m (20ft); they often become detached and even then can continue to sting. Juveniles of Haddock, Saithe and whiting live among the stinging tentacles for protection, seemingly impervious to the stings.

1 Squirrel's Tail

2 Plumed Hydroid

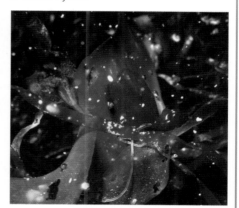

3 Sea Feather (*above*)
4 Stalked Jellyfish (*above right*)
5 Lion's Mane Jellyfish (*right*)

1 MOON JELLYFISH
Aurelia aurita
The Moon Jellyfish is one of the most common of all the jellyfishes and occurs in every ocean throughout the world. Recognized by the four purplish or blue gonad rings found on the top of the bell, it can grow to up to 40cm (15.7in) in diameter. The bell is surrounded by a ring of small tentacles. This species of jellyfish is not harmful to humans, and preys on small fishes and other planktonic larvae. It uses the sun as a compass and forms breeding aggregations in late summer followed by extensive mutual migration into shallow coastal waters. The sedentary stage of the Moon Jellyfish is found under rocky overhangs well aerated by tidal movement and releases young medusa into open waters in spring.

2 CROSSED JELLYFISH
Aqueorea aequorea
Although this is a similar species to the Moon Jellyfish, *Aurelia aurita*, it is distinguished by the pale cross over the bell, as opposed to the four circles on the Moon Jellyfish. It is saucer-shaped, being thicker in the centre and thinning out towards the edges, where there are up to 160 marginal tentacles. The Crossed Jellyfish can grow to approximately 10cm (4in) in diameter and moves fairly actively in the water column by pulses of the bell. It is widely distributed in the northern North Sea and Norwegian Sea, and feeds on other planktonic creatures.

3 BELL JELLYFISH
Rhizostoma octopus
One of the largest of the jellyfishes found floating around in plankton, the outer bell of this species can be over 1m (3ft 3in) in diameter. Very solid in construction, it over-winters in deeper water and migrates into the North Sea from the Atlantic. It has eight short, clubbed tentacles that are subdivided into numerous frilled mouths, and employs a mucus coating to trap food particles. It varies in colour from whitish pale or yellow to shades of green, blue, pink or brown. The Bell Jellyfish is found in coastal waters and is frequently stranded on the shore or in rockpools by receding tides.

4 BOLINOPSIS
Bolinopsis infundibulum
The largest ctenophore to be found in northern European waters, the Bolinopsis can grow to up to 15cm (5.9in) in diameter. It is quite delicate and ovoid in shape, with four long and four short rows of swimming combs of cilia. It also has two large, jelly-like lobes and is almost totally transparent with a bluish tinge. The Bolinopsis is preyed upon by other ctenophores and jellyfishes.

5 SEA GOOSEBERRY
Pleurobrachia pileus
The body of this ctenophore is cylindrical and round, growing to up to 3cm (1.2in) in diameter. Its eight distinct swimming combs extend most of the way around it. Its mouth is located at the bottom, where two very long, feathery tentacles grow: these can reach over 14cm (5½in) in length and it uses them to catch prey. The Sea Gooseberry is a pelagic species that is often blown inshore in the autumn months, where it collects in rockpools. When seen during the night, the swimming cilia of the Sea Gooseberry are iridescent and appear to emit light.

6 STRING JELLY
Apolemia uvaria
This is a curious jellyfish that can reach over 30m (100ft) in length! The String Jelly contains many hundreds of animals with stinging cells arranged in a colonial string. Usually translucent blue in colour, the gonads and egg cases are pale cream or pink, and the stinging cells are dotted with cream spots. The animal is often disjointed from the bulb-like chamber at the 'head' and drifts amid the plankton, feeding as it goes.

7 Neoturris pileata
This lovely bell-shaped jellyfish is oceanic in origin, sweeping into the North Sea from the Atlantic. It has a ring of corkscrewing tentacles that it can let out and retract whenever it is catching prey. Its reproductive organs are pale pink and clearly visible within the translucent bell of the animal, which grows to around 5cm (2in) in height.

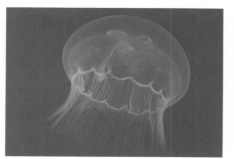

1 Moon Jellyfish

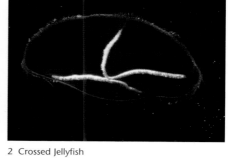

2 Crossed Jellyfish

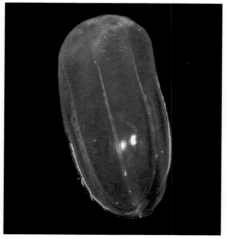

4 Bolinopsis

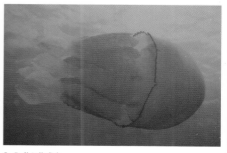

3 Bell Jellyfish

5 Sea Gooseberry

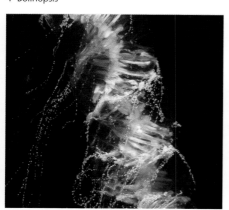

6 String Jelly

7 *Neoturris pileata*

HEXACORALLIA

This subdivision of the zoanthids is the largest family group and includes the zoanthids, anemones and corals. The name indicates that the polyp tentacles are arranged in groups of six, rather than eight. Most anemones are solitary and attach to a hard substrate by means of a basal sucker. Others burrow into soft sand or mud, creating a protective tube into which they can withdraw. Some species favour living in close proximity due to the nature of their reproduction. Others produce live young. Some reproduce by basal laceration, where part of the column or base is detached and grows into a new polyp.

All anemones are carnivorous, trapping unwary small fishes or invertebrates within the sticky grasp of their tentacles. However, many creatures are seemingly immune to the stinging cells and live within the range of the tentacles for protection from other predators.

ZOANTHIDS

1 SANDY CREEPLET
Epizoanthus couchii
This zoanthid is distinguished by its 24–32 long, transparent tentacles, each of which has a small, opaque white knob at the end. It forms small beds or aggregations between the edge of the sand and the rock face, usually in depths below 9m (30ft). It favours swift-moving water, and while it is primarily a southern species found in France and Belgium, it is also located in the northern British Isles and Scandinavia.

ANEMONES

2 BEADLET ANEMONE
Actinia equina
The most common of the shallow-water anemones, the Beadlet Anemone is found throughout the North Sea region. It is usually left exposed at low tide or found in shallow rockpools. It can grow to about 6cm (2.3in) tall and the same in diameter. The column is smooth and the oral disc has 192 tentacles in 5–6 rows, which can be quickly retracted. Below the disc and sometimes formed as part of the collar, there are 24 hollow warts that are usually vivid blue in colour. These warts contain stinging cells with which this species will attack other anemones of the same species if they start to invade its space. The Beadlet Anemone produces live young. An adult lifts its new 'babies' from inside the body cavity on the end of one of its tentacles and places them around itself.

3 BURROWING ANEMONE
Cerianthus lloydii
This is the most common of the burrowing anemones in the area, inhabiting sea lochs, fjords, areas of strong tidal current, gravel, sand and rocky seabeds. It is cylindrical and grows to over 20cm (7.8in). Often found in huge aggregations, only the top third is ever visible. The oral disc has over 60 brownish-white tentacles up to 5cm (1.9in) long, in two rows that cannot be withdrawn.

4 SNAKELOCKS ANEMONE
Anemonia viridis
Quite rare in northern waters, this species is more commonly associated with the Mediterranean and the southern and western shores of the British Isles. It grows to up to 19cm (7½in) across and is instantly recognizable by its 'gorgon-like' head of around 200 tentacles, which it is unable to retract. Generally grey or greenish in colour with purple-tipped tentacles, it is found on the lower shore or deeper hard substrates, where it is associated with a number of small crabs and gobies.

5 DEEPWATER DAHLIA
Urticina eques
This large anemone is similar to the Dahlia Anemone, *U. felina*, but it does not have a sticky column; it does have inconspicuous white, warty tubercles. It prefers deeper water, usually below 18m (60ft), and attaches itself to stones and even gravel. The oral disc may grow to 30cm (12in), with tentacles up to 6cm (2½in) long. Very vivid in colour, they are sometimes banded and coloured in shades of red, pink and purple. The oral disc may be paler in colour, but has darker lines around the base of each tentacle.

1 Sandy Creeplet

2 Beadlet Anemone

3 Burrowing Anemone (*above*)
4 Snakelocks Anemone (*right*)
5 Deepwater Dahlia (*below*)

1 DAHLIA ANEMONE
Urticina felina

The column of this distinctive anemone is short and squat, and covered in sticky tubercles. The species is noted for the bits of shell and other debris that are attached to the column, so that when the creature closes up it is well camouflaged. The column is relatively dull in colour, but generally multicoloured. The true beauty of this anemone is revealed when its tentacles are fully infused with water and open wide. The colours range from crimson to blue, brown, yellow and everything else in between, quite often on the same animal. The tentacles are short and stout – arranged in multiples of ten, they are very similar to those of the Deepwater Dahlia, *U. eques*. This species prefers shallower water, however, and may often be found in crevices and pools all around the shores of the North Sea.

2 PLUMOSE ANEMONE
Metridium senile

One of the widest ranging temperate-waters anemone, the Plumose Anemone is found in all regions of the North Sea and extends through Iceland, Greenland and North America. There are two varieties, one large and one small. This is a rather beautiful anemone in shades of white or orange, often with a column that is a sickly green colour. When fully exposed and reaching as high as 45cm (1½ft), the column is smooth but for tiny holes where stinging threads can be ejected. There is a distinct collar of over 200 small tentacles underneath the crown. They are so numerous that they form a distinct fluffy or plumed appearance, hence the common name of this anemone. It grows almost anywhere, from shipwrecks to piers and rocky reefs, and reproduces asexually by pedal laceration.

3 ELEGANT ANEMONE
Sagartia elegans

This species has an incredibly diverse colour range, and individuals of different colours can quite often be found directly next to each other. The common denominators are that the columns always have warty tubercles, are generally reddish-brown and slightly spotted and are tall and slender, with the widest part being across the oral disc. The oral disc has over 200 tentacles arranged in several rings, and the anemones grow to around 6cm (2in) in height. When irritated, they eject sticky white threads. They are found on exposed rocky shores and headlands, and their range extends from rockpools to depths of around 50m (165ft) in all areas of the North Sea, including Scandinavia.

4 CLOAK ANEMONE
Adamsia carciniopados

A truly adaptive species, the Cloak Anemone wraps itself around the shell inhabited by the hermit crab *Pagarus prideaux*. The column of the anemone is pale fawn with garish magenta spots, and the oral disc contains over 500 small tentacles. The disc is usually found on the bottom of the crab's shell and enjoys the crab's messy leftovers. Its size depends on the shell it covers. When threatened, it secretes long, sticky, magenta threads.

5 JEWEL ANEMONE
Corynactis viridis

This tiny, extremely colourful anemone is very common in the south-west of the British Isles and western islands. The North Atlantic drift has assured that it has a much wider distribution than it was once thought to have. It enjoys low sunlight and nutrient-rich water, and will often frame the entrances to caverns or inhabit deep fissures. The polyps reach a maximum size of only 12mm (½in), and the anemone is invariably very easy to spot due to its iridescent bright colours. The short tentacles are characterized by their knobbly tips. The Jewel Anemone is able to reproduce asexually and many individuals of the same colour form are found together, often forming large sheets of colour.

6 PEACHIA
Peachia cylindrica

Also known as *P. hastata*, this is a non-attached burrowing anemone that is rather robust and may reach 30cm (1ft) in length and 2.5cm (1in) in diameter. It has a light-coloured disc with about 12 characteristically light-coloured tentacles ribbed with deeper V-shaped brown markings. It is only the disc and tentacles that are visible – the rest of the animal is hidden below the sand or gravel seabed.

1 Dahlia Anemone

2 Plumose Anemone

3 Elegant Anemone

4 Cloak Anemone

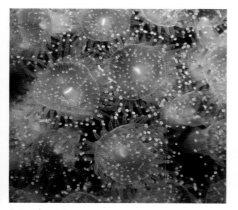

5 Jewel Anemone

6 Peachia

1 TURRET SHELL ANEMONE
Sagartiogeton laceratus
This small anemone inhabits muddy and fine sand seabeds, and is usually found in association with scallops and turret shells. It is a small, slender anemone measuring about 2.5cm (1in), brown in colour with a ring of short tentacles. It is found in all northern tidal but sheltered regions of the North Sea.

2 EELGRASS ANEMONE
Sagartiogeton viduatus
The Eelgrass Anemone has a limited distribution principally around the Eelgrass beds in southern Norway. The one shown here was photographed on seagrass off Kristiansand in southeast Norway. It is rarely larger than 1.5 cm (¾in) in height, and olive-green in colour with lengthways pale orange or yellow stripes. The tentacles are usually greyish or whitish in colour.

3 PINK ANEMONE
Bolocera tuediae
A large anemone with ribbed, pink tentacles that it is able to shed if attacked by predators, the Pink Anemone grows to over 15cm (6in) across. It prefers a well-aerated but tidal area with hard rock as a base, and has a symbiotic or commensal relationship with the Northern Prawn, *Pandalus borealis*. This is a distinctly northern species found exclusively in the North Sea from the Berwickshire coast of Scotland across into Scandinavia.

4 SMALL PINK ANEMONE
Protanthea simplex
This species is very rare on the east coast of the British Isles, and the author was the first person to record it living in the sea lochs of the Scottish west coast. The column of the anemone is flattened and has a lightly adherent disc that flares out at the margins. This small pink-coloured, relatively translucent anemone is found abundantly in northern waters, particularly in many of the Norwegian fjords. It grows to approximately 20mm (¾in) high and has 200 barely retractable pale tentacles, which are capable of being shed should any danger threaten. The Small Pink Anemone is also known to be very active and is quite mobile over its habitat, being found attached to sea squirts, worm tubes, dead corals, seaweeds, bare rock and indeed, pretty well anything that does not have locomotion.

CORALS
The corals found around the shores of the North Sea are usually of the single or solitary polyp variety. There may be large, extensive colonies attached to hard rocky surfaces or even shipwrecks. Due to the relatively low water temperatures of this region, the large stony corals associated with the tropical coral reefs are not found here. However, the region also supports a number of sea fans and a similar species of soft coral.

5 DEVONSHIRE CUP CORAL
Caryophyllia smithii
One of the few true corals that inhabit northern waters, this familiar species has a large single polyp with up to 80 translucent, knobbly-ended tentacles. The deeply grooved, calcified disc is approximately 15mm (½in) in diameter. As in all cup coral species, the tentacles can be retracted, allowing the calcified exterior to offer full protection to the animal.

6 COMMUNAL CUP or CARPET CORAL
Hoplangia durotrix
The Communal Cup Coral looks like the Devonshire Cup Coral, *Caryophyllia smithii*, in every way, except that it consists of a small group of single polyps clumped together into four or five seemingly joined animals that are in fact disjointed. Each polyp has a ring of knobbly feeding tentacles. The Communal Cup Coral is mostly associated with the south coast of England and the very north of Scotland, Shetland Isles and Scandinavia, although it ranges as far south as the Farne Islands off the Northumberland coast of England.

1 Turret Shell Anemone

3 Pink Anemone

2 Eelgrass Anemone

4 Small Pink Anemone

5 Devonshire Cup Coral (*above*)
6 Communal Cup Coral (*left*)

OCTOCORALLIA

Octocorallia is a successful group of animals that includes the soft corals, sea fans and sea pens. They are very similar to the anemones and true corals, but have eight feeding tentacles as opposed to six. The medusoid stage in octocorals has been suppressed, and all the animals represented in the North Sea zone are in fact colonies consisting of loosely connected polyps.

1 DEAD MAN'S FINGERS
Alcyonium digitatum

This soft coral grows in an irregular branched manner, forming the blunt 'fingers' that give it its name. Overall white or pale orange in colour, the polyps are always white, and the coral can grow to up to 25cm (10in) in height. Each polyp has eight tentacles, with which it feeds on passing plankton. It grows attached to exposed rocky surfaces, shipwrecks and oil- and gas-rig support legs in relatively strong currents below the 6m (20ft) level.

SEA FANS

Sea fans are relatively rare in northern latitudes. They like deep, swift-moving water, which enables their polyps to collect food particles. They form an erect column of individuals, in a fan made of an intricate web of dividing branches that stretch out across the current.

2 NORTHERN SEA FAN
Swiftia pallida

This is a relatively slender, stalked species with only a few irregular branching arms. Growing to around 20cm (8in) in length, it is generally white in colour. The polyps are sometimes pale cream, and are arranged asymmetrically. The species inhabits deep vertical walls and is generally found below 25m (80ft).

3 WARTY SEA FAN
Eunicella verrucosa

This species is richly branched and will form a wide fan shape, somewhat like a true gorgonian, up to 30cm (11.8in) in length. Protruding out from the branches, the polyps are white in colour without any pattern, and are arranged in double rows towards the tips. This

distinctive species inhabits southern localities and is always a delight to find because there are so few true corals in the North Sea. It prefers relatively sheltered conditions.

SEA PENS

Sea pens are a curious relation in this group, living in deep water on a fine substrate, yet preferring currents that allow them to spread their net-like arms of polyps. They are able to totally retract into the substrate when danger threatens. Sea pens tend to hide under soft sediments during the day, and extend their soft bodies by infusing water and stretching upwards to feed at night.

4 TALL SEA PEN
Funiculina quadrangularis

The tallest of the sea pens found in the North Sea region, this species has been recorded in the north-western British Isles and numerous fjords in Norwegian waters. It can grow to as large as 1.7m (5.5ft) in length and is therefore fairly easy to identify. Its stem does not branch, and the polyps sit directly on the stem. This sea pen is usually reddish-yellow or cream in colour, and occurs on soft bottoms below 20m (66ft).

5 SEA PEN
Virgularia mirabilis

A small species up to 17cm (7in) in height, the Sea Pen prefers deeper waters with some current in which to spread its polyps. Found in clusters of three to eight and located in two rows, the polyp and column can turn towards the prevailing current and create a net with which to capture food particles. The Sea Pen prefers a clean, fine, sandy seabed, and is most often associated with sea lochs and fjords.

6 PHOSPHORESCENT SEA PEN
Penneatula phosphorea

Usually pinkish in colour, this species forms a fleshy central column with side branches arranged on a single plane. The polyps are white and the arms only extend to about half of the animal's length, the rest of which is hidden below the sand. When moved suddenly, the animal may flash phosphorescently.

1 Dead Man's Fingers

2 Northern Sea Fan

3 Warty Sea Fan

4 Tall Sea Pen

5 Sea Pen

6 Phosphorescent Sea Pen

BRYOZOANS

Bryozoans are a group of delicate, sessile, colonial animals that contains many different families with equally many characteristics. Each animal in a colony is called a zooid, and the creatures attach to each other by their thin zooid walls. In the North Sea region, most bryozoans are actually in the 'mat' form, or lightly branching, but all of them are quite flexible. Most bryozoans are fed on by a variety of nudibranchs, particularly the Four-lined Nudibranch, *Polycera quadrilineata*.

1 HAIRY SEA MAT
Electra pilosa
The Hairy Sea Mat forms a mat-like encrusting colony, usually branching on various algae including *Laminaria* spp. and various wracks on the seashore. Each zooid has a single long spine or bristle at one edge and a further 11 very small bristles around the edges. The zooids are very squat, only growing to 0.5mm (.2in) in height, but the colonies contain many hundreds or even thousands of individuals.

2 SEA MAT
Membranipora membranacea
This is the most common of all the sea mats within the North Sea zone and it is widely distributed everywhere. The colonies can be quite extensive and encrust the large fronds of *Laminaria* spp. The zooids are rectangular in shape with short tubercles at the corners. Colonies are a greyish-white in colour, and the leading edge forms a white band that is fed upon by a number of nudibranchs and small snails.

3 HORNWRACK
Flustra foliacea
The Hornwrack is characterized by stiff, fairly erect, flexible colonies 10–20cm (4–8in) tall with rounded fronds. Looking more like an alga, a colony comprises many thousands of individuals. It is greyish-white in colour, and surprisingly has a lemony scent when found alive on the lower shore. This very common bryozoan can be found from the Barents Sea and Arctic Norway all the way south to the Bay of Biscay.

4 HORNED STRAP WRACK
Securiflustra securifrons
Very similar to the Hornwrack, *Flustra foliacea*, this species of erect bryozoan is arranged more in narrow, strap-like fronds, which are branching and make it appear more like a hydroid or even an alga. It grows to over 20cm (5in) high in deeper water with moderate turbidity and strong tidal movement. It is most common in the northern North Sea and Scandinavia.

5 BUGULA
Bugula turbinata
The Bugula forms dense, tufted colonies. It rises from a single stalk, resembles an alga and is pale cream in colour. Growing to around 4cm (1½in) high, it is often in a spiral form and forms roundish clumps. The tiny zooids have three outer spines and a further two inner spines. It is most common around the British Isles and as far north as Denmark and southern Norway.

6 ERECT BRYOZOAN
Porella compressa
Curiously, this bryozoan was once thought to be found only in the south-west of the British Isles and on the French coast; however, a more stunted version with more defined branches has been found in the Orkney and Shetland Islands, south-east Scotland and southern Norway. It is orange in colour and rigid like a true coral. Each branchlet is lobed and slightly dome-shaped, and it can grow to over 10cm (4in) in length.

7 FINGER BRYOZOAN or SEA CHERVIL
Alcyonidium diaphanum
Highly variable in shape, this bryozoan grows to about 15cm (6in) in length on exposed rock faces underneath the kelp zone. It is usually golden-brown to greenish-beige in colour, and resembles an alga.

1 Hairy Sea Mat

2 Sea Mat

3 Hornwrack

4 Horned Strap Wrack

5 Bugula

6 Erect Bryozoan

7 Finger Bryozoan

WORMS

Many species of worm are found around the North Sea, and the group is as diverse as it is interesting. There are flat, errant worms wandering around in search of food. There are nemertid worms, which are unsegmented and have eyes and a mouth, and are active hunters on reefs. The polychaete worms are sessile and produce a parchment or calcified tube, which they can hide inside when not feeding. There is a curious bristle worm called a Sea Mouse, and finally there are the annelid worms that burrow in soft sand and mud – it is usually their worm castes that you see on the lower shore.

SEGMENTED WORMS

1 FOOTBALL-JERSEY WORM
Tubulanus annulatus
Strikingly marked with both a mid-dorsal stripe and transverse white rings around a brown or orange-red body, this worm can reach about 60cm (2ft) in length. It is occasionally found under stones on the lower shore and lives in a wide range of habitats; it is often seen around the holdfasts of kelp plants, as well as in muddy or fine sand and gravel sea floor near scallop beds. It occurs throughout the region.

2 BOOTLACE WORM
Lineus longissimus
This species is perhaps the most common Nemertean worm living among stones and seaweeds, both intertidally and sub-tidally, in all regions of the North Sea and its bordering countries. It is generally a rich reddish-brown in colour with lighter longitudinal stripes, and can reach over 45cm (18in) in length; in some extreme cases it has been known to be over 30m (100ft) long. Amazingly, one was even measured at 55m (180ft), making it the longest animal in the world! It is, however, only 10mm (¼in) in width. Very flexible, it is able to retract into a hole or crevice when danger threatens. To feed, it extends a cluster of sticky filaments and uses these to immobilize prey.

3 SEA MOUSE
Aphrodite aculeate
This segmented worm grows to about 20cm (8in) long and has an elongated, oval body covered in fine greyish hairs. It gets its common name of Sea Mouse mainly due to its coloration. Its flanks are its most distinctive feature: they have iridescent green or golden bristles and lustrous brown spines. An active hunter on soft sand and mud, the Sea Mouse burrows into the substrate to escape predators or to look for food. Usually found sub-tidally, it can also occur on the lower shore during extreme spring tides. It is most commonly associated with sea lochs and fjords, and prefers a mud or fine sand substrate.

4 BRISTLE WORM
Harmathoë impar
A small worm commonly found on kelp, this species is about 5cm (2in) long and has quite distinct, hairy legs. Its abdomen is rounded and slightly flattened, with prominent tentacles and a clearly forked tail.

5 PALE BRISTLE WORM
Alentia gelatinosa
This small, oval bristle worm is pale cream in colour and grows to about 12mm (½in) in length. It prefers a rough gravel and stone or shell debris seabed, where it hides under stones or in empty shells. There is a series of overlapping plates all along its back. When disturbed, it rolls partially into a ball in a similar way to a woodlouse.

6 LUG WORM
Arenicola marina
This common species is reddish-brown in colour and averages around 11cm (4½in) in length. Its sand 'casts', seen on the lower sandy shore, are what point to its presence. A popular bait for fishermen, it is now protected in some areas.

1 Football-jersey
Worm (*above*)
2 Bootlace Worm
(*above right*)

3 Sea Mouse
(*right*)
4 Bristle Worm
(*below*)

5 Pale Bristle Worm

6 Lug Worm

1 RAG WORM
Hediste diversicolor

The Rag Worm grows to about 12.5cm (5in) long and has a rather flattened, soft body. Usually orange or brownish-red in colour, during spawning the colour changes to a greenish-brown, but this may just be from the colour of the eggs showing through the mantle. The Rag Worm has very short, paired tentacles or parapodia, which it uses for swimming or crawling, and has a distinctive red blood vessel along the entire length of its flattened body. It has four pairs of tentacles, two antennae and two palps on its head. Found on the lower sandy shore when the tide is far out, it is frequently used as bait by sea-anglers. It lives in a relatively permanent, U-shaped burrow at a depth of about 20cm (8in); this has an obvious depression at one end and coiled whorls of sand at the other. The Rag Worm is very widespread in brackish water and is found throughout north-western Europe. There has been some controversy over the correct scientific name to be applied to this species, and *Nereis diversicolor* is still used by many authors.

SEDENTARY WORMS

2 PEACOCK WORM
Sabella pavonina

The Peacock Worm is a common species that generally inhabits soft sand or mud in sheltered, low-light conditions. It will also attach itself to deeper shipwrecks and rock walls in areas of moving water. The tube is of parchment construction and is quite stiff. The head of the fan is about 7cm (2½in) in diameter and is coloured in shades of brown and orange in concentric rings, giving a pleasant effect when viewed. The fan is light-and pressure-sensitive, and quickly retracted inside the tube if danger threatens. The Peacock Worm appears quite at home in all regions of the North Sea and all habitats.

3 SALMACINA CORAL WORM
Salmacina dysteri

The Salmacina Coral Worm is a curious tube worm that forms large colonies of intertwined, tiny calcareous tubes about 6mm (¼in) long. The tubes of the creatures are white and almost translucent, and interweave as they grow into a rope-like mass. Each worm has about 30 body segments, and the head has eight pinkish tentacles and is not protected by a chitonous cup like that of the almost identical Delicate Coral Worm, *Filograna implexa*. The Salmacina Coral Worm can be found on rocks and generally only sublittorally in tide-swept or surge areas.

4 DELICATE CORAL WORM
Filograna implexa

The Delicate Coral Worm is one of the most delicate of the tube-worm species. It grows in interlacing colonies that are over 15cm (6in) in diameter, and its calcareous protective tubes are only 1–2mm (about ⅟₁₆in) in diameter. Often found around various bryozoans, the fan tuft is only 6mm (¼in) across and its base is pale yellow or orange. The worm has eight tentacles each with thirty bristles that form the tuft. Extremely fragile, the tubes are very vulnerable to damage. Another identification point is that the tubes are bifurcating because this species has asexual reproduction, in which the 'father' divides into two parts and carries the fertilized eggs in one of the tubes. In this way, the colony quickly expands. A real gregarious cosmopolitan, the Delicate Coral Worm is found throughout the North Sea and Atlantic and as far north as North Cape, the northernmost point of Finnmark.

5 SMALL TUBE WORM
Pomatocerous triqueter

Often overlooked due to its small size, this tiny tube worm is quite common on the lower shore and can be found on many stone and rocky surfaces, including shells and the carapaces of some species of decapod. It is characterized by having an obvious diamond-shaped tube, which is often overgrown by algae. The mouth of the tube can be tinged from green to red. The spiral fan tuft is spotted and can be virtually any colour, from white and blue to green and purple. The raised calcareous tubes of the Small Tube Worm are usually curled and about 5cm (2in) in length.

1 Rag Worm

2 Peacock Worm

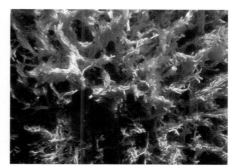

3 Salmacina Coral Worm

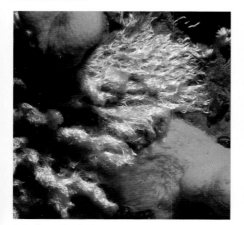

4 Delicate Coral Worm

5 Small Tube Worm

1 SPIRAL WORM
Spirorbis spirorbis

This is a small, tube-dwelling polychaete worm with a sinistrally coiled (left-handed) tube that is smooth and white with a prominent lip. It is frequently found in small aggregations on the surfaces of wracks and other types of seaweed. The Spiral Worm is only about 3mm (.1in) in length and is segmented, with a tail, thorax and head, and two gills that are composed of transparent filaments.

2 SAND MASON
Lanice conchilega

This curious worm has a body around 30cm (11.8in) long, but it is only the tubes of the tentacles that you are likely to see, sticking up about 5cm (2in) above the seabed. This polychaete worm is usually pale yellow, pink or brown in colour, and has three pairs of bushy gills that are blood red in colour. The segmented body has between 150 and 200 sections, with 17 segments in the front section. The Sand Mason forms a tube of pieces of gravel and other shell detritus around the upper part of its body and cements tiny particles of sand onto the tubes containing the retractile tentacles – this is where its common name comes from. The frayed end protrudes above the sand like a fan and is aligned across the path of the tidal stream, enabling it to trap food particles.

3 INQUISITIVE TUBE WORM or STRAWBERRY WORM
Eupolymnia nebulosa

Often overlooked by divers, the Inquisitive Tube Worm's body is always hidden beneath the substrate or in a hole, with only its long, pale blue or white translucent tentacles seen fanning out over the surface, where it looks for detritus as food. The tentacles can be over 15cm (6in) long, and are sticky to touch. The body is rounded, soft and fragile and about 1cm (.39in) long, and has over 200 tentacles. The posterior end is generally in a coil and the anterior end has two pairs of branched gills, but it is usually only the tentacles that are observed. Although its tube is rarely seen, this is a tube-building polychaete worm and its worm tubes have been found in many Norwegian locations. The Inquisitive Tube Worm is common throughout the North Sea zone.

4 VARIABLE TUBE WORM or RED TUBE WORM
Serpula vermicularis

This species is very distinctive in colour, ranging from brilliant orange to purple. It is only 2cm (¾in) in diameter and slightly horseshoe-shaped. The protective cap (operculum) of its calcified tube home is clearly visible. Inhabiting rocky walls, stones, bivalve shells and even ships' hulls, the Variable Tube Worm prefers low light in well-aerated water. In sheltered areas, this sublittoral species can grow in depths of 250m (820ft), and can form aggregations of small, reef-like structures. The tube is a creamy-pink in colour, generally patterned with white and red rays, and can be up to 10cm (3.93in) in length. It is usually rambling or slightly coiled. The Variable Tube Worm is light- and pressure-sensitive, quickly retracting its feeding fan if danger approaches. It is an uncommon species in the North Sea, but its distribution extends around the British Isles, Denmark and the Norwegian coast; it is often found on semi-permanent floats, pier pilings and even shells.

5 MUD WORM
Myxicola infundibulum

Quite distinctive in appearance, the Mud Worm favours a mud or soft sand sublittoral habitat in depths down to 30m (100ft), often at the entrances to caves and caverns. It prefers wave-sheltered areas and can quite often be found in estuarine mud, where the salinity varies. It is a stout, segmented worm that is dark yellow or ochre in colour, about 20cm (8in) long and lives in a permanent mucilaginous tube, always buried beneath the surface. The crown is generally purplish-grey in colour, and the protruding fan is crater-like in appearance and is quickly retracted if danger threatens, reducing its size by half. The tips of the fan are dark brown, and the overall length of the worm is about 3cm (1¼in). Surprisingly versatile in its distribution, the Mud Worm is found all around the British Isles, Scandinavia and even across the Atlantic in Newfoundland.

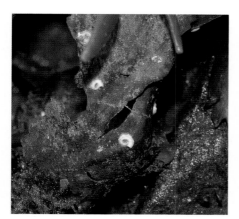

1 Spiral Worm

2 Sand Mason

3 Inquisitive Tube Worm

4 Variable Tube Worm

5 Mud Worm

CRUSTACEANS (FAMILY CRUSTACEA)

This large family has over 30,000 members worldwide, and crustaceans are found in every marine habitat. In general they have segmented bodies with head, thorax and abdomen, and are heavily protected by calcareous outer body armour. Most divers see the obvious decapod species that have ten legs. Depending on the species, the legs are adapted for walking, feeding, swimming, defence, food capture, respiration and even the carrying of eggs. This wide and varied group includes barnacles, shrimps, lobsters, hermit crabs and crabs.

BARNACLES

1 COMMON BARNACLE
Balanus balanus
This is one of the most common barnacles, found almost everywhere throughout the region. It grows to up to 2cm (¾in) in length and is roughly circular shaped, with a shell made up of six overlapping, irregularly sized and deeply ridged white plates. It is found on the lower shore on rocks, stones, old shells, ships' hulls and even the shells of crabs, lobsters and scallops. Its distribution range includes Iceland, Norway, Denmark, northern Europe and most of the British Isles.

2 Balanus crenatus
A big intertidal barnacle, this species grows in large aggregations and has a maximum size of about 25mm (1in). It has six plate walls that are usually pale and smooth and only slightly ridged. Whenever the barnacle becomes detached it leaves the circular mark of an obvious basal plate behind on the rock.

SHRIMPS

3 ELEGANT SHRIMP
Palaemon elegans
This is one of the most common shrimps found around the coastline and it is normally associated with a rocky substrate. Quite a stout animal, it grows to about 6cm (2½in) long and has strong reddish-brown stripes on a fairly transparent body. It is often found in association with Dead Man's Fingers, *Alcyonium digitatum*, and prefers low-light conditions – it is an active forager by dusk and at night-time.

4 PINK SHRIMP
Palaemon montagui
The Pink Shrimp is relatively large, growing to up to 15cm (6in) in length. The body is semi-transparent, and there are patches of red around both head and body. The carapace has a long, upturned rostrum with 10–12 very small spines attached and an additional spine just below the eye. The species is widely distributed in all regions of the North Sea in depths of 6m (20ft) and below.

5 BROWN SHRIMP
Crangon crangon
This is a rather squat species with a short, blunt head, but with two long antennae as long as its 9cm (4½in) body. It is fairly transparent and a mottled greyish-brown in colour. The first two pairs of legs are quite short and bear small claws, and the third and fourth pairs are the longest. This species prefers a fine sandy seabed.

6 HARLEQUIN SHRIMP
Hippolyte varians
The Harlequin Shrimp grows to 35mm (1½in) in length and occurs in a wide range of habitats around all northern regions of the North Sea. It can be found living on hydroids and many species of algae, including *Laminaria* spp. and *Halydris* spp. Varying hugely in colour, it may be brown, red, blotched or green. It may also have small, hair-like filaments attached that act as camouflage. The carapace is long and straight, the slightly upturned rostrum has one single spine and the front two legs bear feeding pincers. This species appears to breed at any time of the year and is found from the lower shore and deeper rockpools down to 50m (165ft).

1 Common Barnacle

2 *Balanus crenatus*

3 Elegant Shrimp

4 Pink Shrimp

5 Brown Shrimp

6 Harlequin Shrimp

1 LONG-SPINE or PEPPERMINT SHRIMP

Hippolyte longirostris

Only growing to 20mm (¾in) in length, as the common name of this species suggests it has a long rostrum – in fact one that is almost as long as its carapace. It is usually greenish-brown or reddish-brown in colour, but is primarily identified by the iridescent blue spots that can be seen along its body. It inhabits relatively shallow water and appears to use *Halydris* as its main home.

2 WHITE-STRIPE SHRIMP

Hippolyte inermis

One of the largest shrimps in the *Hippolyte* genus, the White-stripe Shrimp can grow to almost 50mm (2in) in length. While it is variable in colour from green to brownish-red, all individuals have a broad white or cream stripe running along the entire length of the body, as well as blue spots along the flanks. Once presumed to be quite scarce, it would appear that this species is found much further than was believed: it has a range from Norway, south to the Atlantic Moroccan coast, through the Mediterranean and into the Black Sea.

3 ARCTIC ICE SHRIMP

Eualus gaimardii

This species is distinguished by its fairly transparent to slightly pinkish-tinged body, and the fact that it stores its green egg mass within its head cavity. Normally it would never be seen or identified without this tell-tale description. It can grow to as much as 10cm (4in) long, but is usually much smaller. Its rostrum is pointed, bent and almost transparent. Its food consists mainly of pelagic decapods and amphipods, but it also feeds on the seabed, where it is known to sift mud for organisms. Circumpolar in its distribution, a huge amount of scientific work has been done on this small shrimp as it feeds amid the Arctic ice flows that get swept into the Gulf of St Lawrence. It is also well known in Washington State, Norway, Finland, the Baltic and most northern regions of the North Sea. It was named after the French surgeon, naturalist, ichthyologen and zoologist Joseph Paul Gaimard.

LOBSTERS

4 COMMON or EUROPEAN LOBSTER

Homarus gammarus

The Common Lobster prefers to live under large boulders or in deep, rocky crevices, but when young it burrows under small stones and lives under the sand. A nocturnal feeder, it is a large, robust animal, bluish in colour with stout pincers, one of which is modified for gripping, the other for cutting; it can be either right- or left-handed! It is a desirable crustacean in the commercial food market and rarely reaches a ripe old age. It can live to over 25 years and reach over 1m (3ft 3in) in length. Lobsters are by nature solitary and territorial, and defend their crevices vigorously. They seek a mate during the summer months and the female carries the eggs under her abdomen for 11 months. When the eggs hatch the juveniles spend 2–3 weeks in the plankton before settling on the seabed, where they burrow into the soft substrate. Two years later, when their carapaces reach about 15mm (.4in), they find a suitable crevice to live in. This species is distributed throughout the eastern Atlantic Ocean and North Sea, and is caught as far north as the Lofoton Islands, west to the Azores, south to Morocco and east into the Baltic, Mediterranean and Black Sea.

5 NORWAY LOBSTER, SCAMPI or LANGOUSTINE

Nephrops norvegicus

This small lobster lives in large, interlaced burrows under soft sand and mud. Pale orange to light tan in colour with transverse stronger coloration over the body segments, the animal usually grows to up to 24cm (9in) in length. However, some super-sized animals over 38cm (15in) have been caught in traps, making them rivals of the Common Lobster, *Homarus gammarus*. The striking Norway Lobster has two large pincers and a secondary set of smaller feeding pincers. It has relatively long antennae and jet black eyes, and prefers dark, deep-water habitats. The species has a symbiotic relationship with the Fries' Goby, *Lesueribobius friesii*, and is found throughout the northern North Sea.

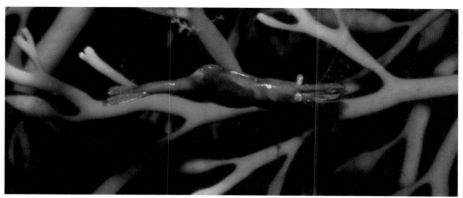

1 Long-spine Shrimp

2 White-stripe Shrimp

3 Arctic Ice Shrimp

4 Common Lobster

5 Norway Lobster

1 ALGAE SQUAT LOBSTER
Galathea dispersa

As its name suggests, this squat lobster is most commonly found on various species of kelp, wrack and sea pod. It is dull red to orange in colour with transverse lighter lines across the carapace. The claws and legs are hairy and have several very sharp spines on the inside edges. The abdominal segment is deeply grooved and the females carry the eggs in the spring months. The Algae Squat Lobster is found throughout the North Sea region.

2 HAIRY-CLAWED SQUAT LOBSTER
Galathea nexa

This is a strikingly coloured small squat lobster, only growing to about 40mm (1½in) long (including claws). The claws are half the overall length and are 'fuzzy' in appearance with large spikes on the insides of the joints, hence the common name of the species. An overall orange-red in colour with numerous darker blotches on the carapace, the lobster also has small blue markings where the legs join to the main body. It is common around all of the North Sea coastline, usually at depths of below 15m (50ft). The most common observations I have made have been on a stony seabed gulley between hard rock canyons.

3 STRIDENT SQUAT LOBSTER
Galathea strigosa

Certainly the most colourful of all the squat lobsters found in the North Sea region, this species is characterized by a brilliant orange-red colour with vivid blue-striped markings around the eyes and stripes across the carapace. It grows to a maximum length of about 10cm (4in) and prefers low light conditions. It is an active feeder at night and enjoys the company of Leopard-spotted Gobies, *Thorogobius ephippiatus*. All species of squat lobster are heavily predated upon by all manner of fishes, and this understandably makes them not only extremely nervous, but also very swift in their movements – by flicking their tail parts rapidly, they are able to scatter quickly into a sheltered crevice in the rocks when the need arises. They are more closely related to hermit crabs than to the true lobsters.

4 LONG-CLAWED SQUAT LOBSTER
Munida rugosa

The Long-clawed Squat Lobster favours a deep-water habitat, where it lives under stones and rocks. Often associated with brittlestar beds and ascidians, it is instantly recognizable by its bright orange-red coloration, fairly slim body, which can be as long as 30cm (12in), and chelipeds or pincer arms that are twice as long as the body length. Most commonly recorded in the British Isles from the west coast sea lochs, it is also common down the east coast of Scotland in depths of over 15m (50ft). It occurs in the Norwegian fjords, and in some areas is harvested commercially. It is a very social animal that tends to live in large colonies. Female Long-clawed Squat Lobsters carry their eggs under their abdomens in the colder months before releasing the larvae into the planktonic water column. The larvae spend about 2–3 weeks in the water column, before settling down in some rocky crevice or other suitable habitat.

CRABS

HERMIT CRABS

5 COMMON HERMIT CRAB
Pagarus bernhardus

This species is very common on all shores and the sublittoral region of the North Sea from Iceland southwards. It is usually greyish-red in colour with reddish-brown pincers. The claws are ridged and toothed, and the right claw is larger than the left. The crab has further small feeding claws on the next three pairs of legs.

6 PRIDEAUX'S HERMIT CRAB
Pagarus prideaux

This species is mainly associated with the Commensal Anemone, *Adamsia carciniapados*, which completely envelops its carrier shell. The crab is speckled with white and tinged with mauve, and is a light tan colour overall with pinkish striped legs and striped eye-stalks. It grows to up to 3cm (1¼in) in length, and the females lay eggs throughout the summer season. The eggs are bright gold and are kept within the confines of the shell home until the crab releases the larvae.

1 Algae Squat Lobster

3 Strident Squat Lobster

2 Hairy-clawed Squat Lobster

5 Common Hermit Crab

6 Prideaux's Hermit Crab

4 Long-clawed Squat Lobster

SPIDER CRABS

1 GREAT SPIDER CRAB or SEA TOAD
Hyas araneus

This large spider crab has a roughly diamond-shaped carapace up to 7.5cm (3in) across and usually brownish-grey in colour, with small lumps and bumps overall; it is generally lacking in sponge attachments, although the shell has distinctive hooks on both sides of the head with which it may attach algae. Other sessile animals, such as barnacles, may attach to the shell. The crab has large, but short and stout feeding pincers, and is usually found on or around kelp in shallow waters. Considered rare in some areas, the Great Spider Crab is widely distributed throughout the North Sea region. It is found at all depths and in all habitats, and is now known as one of the first invasive species to have reached the Antarctic, first recorded there in 2003. In some areas it is an important commercial species, featuring on the menus in many restaurants.

2 LYRE CRAB
Hyas coarctatus

The carapace of the Sponge Spider Crab is 'lyre-shaped' with a decided 'kink' in the sides, where it narrows behind the eyes. Orange-red in colour, the crab grows to 2.5–6cm (1–4in) across and is generally associated with various sponges and hydroids, which grow over the carapace and even the legs and claws. It is relatively common in all areas of the North Sea, particularly around the British Isles, Denmark and Norway, and is found sublitorally down to over 500m (1,665ft).

3 SCORPION SPIDER CRAB
Inachus dorsettensis

The Scorpion Spider Crab grows to about 2.5cm (1in) across. Its carapace is pear-shaped and light brown or greyish with reddish spots. It has two very short spines on the rostrum and another two just behind the eyes. The carapace is also patterned with small tubercle spines, but these may be hidden by growths of sponges and hydroids that the crab attaches to its back for camouflage, hooking them on the spines. The undersides of its equal-sized claws or chelipeds are pinkish-violet in colour. The Scorpion Spider Crab has a very wide distribution between northern Norway and South Africa. It occurs in coastal waters sublitorally in depths of 4–300m (13–1,000ft), living on a diverse range of substrates ranging from sand and mud to rocky seabeds.

4 LONG-ARMED SPIDER CRAB
Inachus phalangium

This spider crab is very similar to the Scorpion Spider Crab, *I. dorsettensis*, except that it has two very long legs that it always keeps well splayed out at the sides. The legs are usually covered in all sorts of algae fuzz and detritus. This crab also lacks the row of horizontal spines behind the eyes that is characteristic of the Scorpion Spider Crab, and is generally much paler in colour. It is a symbiont of the anemones *Anemonia sulcata* and Snakelocks Anemone, *A. viridis*, and always uses whichever sponges are present in its habitat to attach to its carapace. The Long-armed Spider Crab is found from southern Scandinavia, around all the British coast, south to Mauritania, west to the Azores and Madeira, and east into all regions of the Mediterranean.

5 DESIGNER SPIDER CRAB
Macropodia tenuirostris

This is a small and delicate spider crab. Its carapace is triangular in shape and up to 19mm (¾in) across, and it has a long, pointed rostrum. There are small tubercles on its back that are usually hidden by algae or sponge growth. Its first pair of legs bears short and stout, but weakly developed pincers, while the rest of its legs are long and spindly, often with bits of sponge attached to them. This spider crab is found throughout the North Sea, including all the areas around Denmark, southern Sweden and Norway, and has been recorded as far north as Troms. It is most often found in the tidal zone, but occurs at virtually all depths and in all habitats.

1 Great Spider Crab

2 Lyre Crab

3 Scorpion Spider Crab

4 Long-armed Spider Crab

5 Designer Spider Crab

OTHER CRABS

1 BROAD-CLAWED PORCELAIN CRAB
Porcellana platycheles
The carapace of this species is fairly flat and circular with a protruding blunt rostrum. It is quite small, growing to only 1.5cm (.6in) in length, and has long antennae with a pair of stout pincers, which are usually unequal in size. All of the legs are covered in dense hairs and are commonly brown in colour. The species is found throughout the British Isles and northern Europe to Denmark, and is commonly located under stones on the foreshore in a muddy or soft sand habitat.

2 MASKED or SAND CRAB
Corystes cassivelaunus
This soft sand- and mud-living crab grows to about 7.5cm (3in) in length and has two long antennae that form a breathing tube when the crab is hidden under the surface. Coloured a uniform light tan or pale cream, the carapace is roughly triangular in shape, elongated and may feature patterns that resemble a face (hence the common name of the species). The pincer arms or chelipeds are very long in the male (twice the length of the carapace) and short and stout in the female. This is a burrowing crab, preferring fine sand, and is found at all depths. It feeds on infaunal invertebrates and polychaete worms. The Masked Crab is found throughout the North Sea region, from Norway to Portugal, and its range extends into the Mediterranean and Black Sea.

3 CIRCULAR CRAB
Atelecyclus rotundatus
The almost circular carapace of this crab is about 4cm (1½in) across. It is pale brown in colour, and has a white-dotted, toothed margin and three tooth-like protrusions between the eyes. It has broad, pale, hairy claws with dark brown tips, and all of its legs are hairy. Entirely a sublittoral species, it prefers fine sand or small stones on the seabed. It is often found with its mate in its arms!

4 EDIBLE CRAB
Cancer pagarus
This large, commercially important crab has an oval carapace up to 25cm (10in) across. Brown in colour with a lobed, ridged edge to the carapace, it has a pair of massive claws of similar size that are like the carapace in colour and tipped with black. It inhabits all substrates and is a bottom feeder, living almost entirely off scavenged carcasses. Young individuals tend to favour the intertidal zone, and can be found among stones and rocks, and under various seaweeds. As they mature, they travel deeper and live in all types of marine habitat. The Edible Crab is widely distributed throughout the entire North Sea region to the coast of Denmark and the extreme northern reaches of Norway into the White Sea.

5 SWIMMING or HARBOUR CRAB
Liocarcinus depurator
This is a sandy-coloured swimming crab that is usually around 7.5cm (3in) across the carapace. There are three blunt points between the eyes and the carapace is trapezoid in shape. The pair of claws is ridged and strong, and the paddles on the last pair of legs are usually violet in colour. The Swimming Crab is found in all regions of the North Sea, Denmark, southern Sweden and Norway.

6 BLUE-LEG SWIMMING CRAB
Liocarcinus navigator
The Blue-leg Swimming Crab is a distinctive swimming crab, very similar to the Velvet Swimming Crab, *Necora puber*, and the Swimming Crab, *L. depurator*, but the eyes are more of a dull red in colour than those of the former species, and the space between the eyes is smooth. This species is an overall brown colour, and grows to around 33mm (1.3in) across the carapace, which has numerous transverse, hairy crenulations. The Blue-leg Swimming Crab is quite aggressive, usually opening its claws wide and posturing at divers. Its wide distribution range embraces the northeastern Atlantic from northern Norway to North Africa and the Mediterranean.

1 Broad-clawed Porcelain Crab

2 Masked Crab

3 Circular Crab

4 Edible Crab

5 Swimming Crab

6 Blue-leg Swimming Crab

1 VELVET SWIMMING, FIDDLER or DEVIL CRAB
Necora puber
A species that is characterized by its blood-red, stalked eyes, the Velvet Swimming Crab is very aggressive and fast-moving. It has a brown- to black-edged carapace. Overall, the carapace is bluish in colour, but has a reddish-brown, velvety covering, which hides the blue shell and gives the species its common name. The crab has two strong, equal-sized pincers, also velvety, with which it will not hesitate to defend its territory. Velvet Swimming Crabs live in all types of habitat and usually shelter in a ledge on a rock face, under the protective skirt of an anemone or a recess under a boulder. The carapace is about 5–7.5cm (2–3in) across, and there are ten narrow, unequal tubercles or teeth between the eyes. The hind legs are flattened and covered in hairs – although they are used for swimming, they are not paddle-shaped. Females carry eggs at all times of the year. This species is fished commercially in many areas and is found throughout the entire North Sea zone and beyond.

2 COMMON SHORE or GREEN CRAB, or PARTEN
Carcinus maenus
Generally green in colour, the carapace of this crab can be over 5cm (2in) across and has strong pattern indentations or undulations. The species has a pair of extremely strong pincers and can be quite aggressive if its territory is invaded. Very widespread throughout the entire North Sea region, the Common Shore Crab is found intertidally as well as sublittorally. It lives around seaweeds and the zone between the rocks and the sandy shore, where it hunts for carrion and rotting seaweed.

ISOPODS, AMPHIPODS & RELATED SPECIES

3 ASTACILLA
Astacilla longicornis
This small, brown member of the Crustacea family is not only weird in appearance, but also has a wonderfully complex life. It lives on the stalks of hydroids, and the males grow to about 25mm (1in) in length. Once the female crab hatches her eggs, the young stay attached to her body. When the home of an Astacilla is on the Bottlebrush Hydroid, *Thuiaria thuja*, the cluster of juveniles on the head of the adult makes it look very similar to the hydroid, perhaps acting as camouflage or as a subterfuge to catch small isopods.

4 BALTIC ISOPOD
Idotea baltica
The body of the Baltic Isopod is slightly flattened, slender and oval in shape, and grows to around 3cm (1in) long. Usually purplish-brown in colour, it has a row of small white spots or streaks along the dorsal surface. Its body is segmented and has a pair of flexible antennae, and the rear has three points or teeth. The Baltic Isopod feeds on various algae, which provide it with its coloration. It is widely distributed from the Baltic to the Black Sea.

5 GREEN ISOPOD
Idotea granulosa
The Green Isopod is thin and oval in shape, and flattened at its margins; it tapers off sharply towards its posterior, where there is a blunt point. It grows to up to 2cm (¾in) in length, and is usually a vivid green colour with no other markings – although as in the case of the Baltic Isopod, *I. baltica*, its colour depends on the species of algae it feeds on.

6 JASSA
Jassa falcata
This animal is relatively large, growing to around 12mm (½in) in length, and has a generally flattened appearance. Its head has a pair of small eyes, and it has two long, segmented upper antennae. The first and second legs have pincer-like claws. The Jassa is generally greyish in colour with brown markings on the segmented plates, and can be found on the lower shore and around various algae. Its range includes the warmer waters of the Pacific and Indian Oceans.

1 Velvet Swimming Crab

2 Common Shore Crab

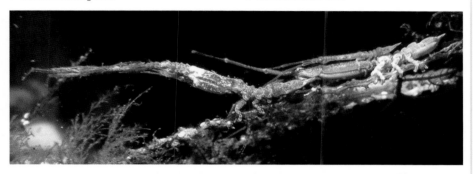

3 Astacilla (*above*)
4 Baltic Isopod
(*right*)

5 Green Isopod

6 Jassa

1 **GHOST** or **SKELETON SHRIMP**
Caprella linearis
Known in Norway as Spøkelseskreps, this little fellow has a slightly cylindrical, long, thin body with fewer appendages than the bodies of other amphipods. Though usually translucent, depending on its habitat it may alternatively be red, green or cream. It reaches about 12mm (½in) in length, and its head bears two pairs of antennae and has a large pair of pincer-like claws. It appears to be non-specific in its habitat and is found attached to kelp, hydroids, Dead Man's Fingers, algae, tunicates and even seagrasses. When feeding, it hooks onto its host with its strong posterior appendages and raises itself up into the water column to catch passing food particles. It is often found in huge numbers, and ranges from the Siberian Polar Sea to all North Sea regions, Iceland, North America, Japan and New Zealand.

2 **OPPOSUM SHRIMP**
Leptomysis gracilis
This species is common among all seaweeds in all regions of the North Sea. It has three pairs of incubatory appendiges or lamellae where its fertilized eggs grow and hatch. Similarly to marsupials, the young are cared for in these pouches until they are ready to fend for themselves. The species grows to about 12mm (½in) long and seems to flit among the algae stalks by means of tiny swimmerettes. Its eyes are well developed and large for such a small crustacean. Its coloration is variable – usually brick-red, it is more often than not quite translucent, with very little pigmentation. The rostrum is long and there is an obvious blunt tip to the thorax, leading to a long tail with a forked end. The species is normally bottom living, usually at the entrances to small crevices, and is found in the company of lobsters and crabs.

3 **PARASITIC GADOID LOUSE**
Caligus elongatus
This very distinctive copepod lives on members of the gadoid family of fishes that includes cod, Haddock, Saithe and Pollack. It attaches itself near the gill openings or mouth, and often underneath the tongue in adult fishes. More often than not, it attachs itself to a juvenile, and will often be almost as long as the poor host. The species has a flattened oval, pointed head, very short body and two long reproductive organs. The head bears two small eyes, and the mouth parts are underneath, where it attaches itself to the host. It is most prevalent in early to late summer, and is found throughout the entire North Sea zone.

SEA SPIDERS

4 **SEA SPIDER**
Nymphon gracile
The body of this sea spider is quite thin and smooth, and it bears a pair of feeding appendages or chelicerae. It has four pairs of walking legs that are three or four times longer than its body, plus a pair of modified legs that in the male's case are used to carry the eggs after they have been laid by the female. Purple-pink in colour, it reaches around 15mm (¾in) in length overall and is usually overlooked due to its small size. It is generally found among bryozoans, hydroids and small anemones.

5 **ANEMONE SEA SPIDER**
Pycogonum littorale
This fellow has a relatively stout body and four pairs of walking legs that look distinctly segmented and end in strongly curved claws. The head is quite long and tapered, but does not bear any feeding chelicerae. Usually pale cream or light brown in colour, the Anemone Sea Spider is generally found attached to prey such as the Dahlia Anemone, *Urticina felina*. It grows to approximately 5mm (¼in) in length.

SAND-HOPPERS

6 **SAND-HOPPER**
Chaetogammarus marinus
A common find on the lower shore, the Sand-hopper usually hides under stones, seaweed and rotting flotsam and jetsam. It can grow to up to 25mm (1in) in length and is generally of varying shades of green or brown, depending on the food it is eating. It is common throughout the North Sea region.

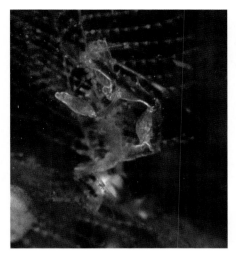

1 Ghost Shrimp

2 Opposum Shrimp

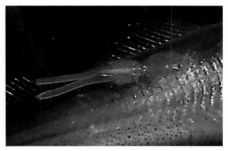

3 Parasitic Gadoid Louse

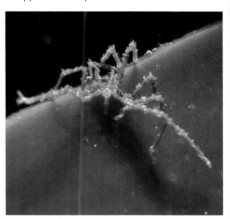

4 Sea Spider

5 Anemone Sea Spider

6 Sand-hopper

MOLLUSCS (FAMILY MOLLUSCA)

The molluscs form the largest and most diverse group of marine animals on the planet, and probably the most familiar group of invertebrates. They include octopus and squid, snails, chitons, bivalves and nudibranchs or sea slugs. There are some 75,000 species in eight families in the world's oceans. Most have common characteristics such as an external shell, a soft body with a muscular foot, and a rasping, tongue-like radula for feeding, with gills of some kind for respiration. All lay eggs, and of the eight groups, five are fairly common around the shores of the North Sea.

CUTTLEFISH, SQUID & OCTOPUS (CEPHALOPODS)

The cephalopods are by far the most successful of the Mollusca, and octopuses are common throughout the North Sea. Extremely intelligent and adaptable, they are free-swimming, fast-moving predators, with well-developed eyes and sensory system. All of the cephalopods are able to change their shape and coloration to suit their environment, or to exhibit and display to a prospective mate or would-be predator. They are also considered prized catches and feature in most coastal seafood restaurants.

1 **COMMON CUTTLEFISH**
Sepia officinalis
This species grows to over 45cm (1ft 6in) in length and has an internal cuttlebone that is a chambered, gas-filled shell used for buoyancy control. Possessing eight arms and two longer feeding tentacles, adults are recognized by the white bands across the body margin and small white spots over the upper surface of the fins. The arms have four rows of suckers and the creature actively stalks prey around seagrass beds and inshore rocky reefs. Like all members of the genus, it is characterized by its ability to change colour and body texture at will. It is primarily found in the southern North Sea region along the French coast.

2 **LITTLE CUTTLEFISH** or **CUTTLEFISH**
Sepiola atlantica
The smallest of the cephalopods in the North Sea, this tiny cuttlefish is usually around 3.5cm (1¼in) long in adulthood. It is plump and round, with rounded large fins that do not run along its entire length. Its colour varies from black-brown to pale dorsally; very rarely it may be striped. It has prominent pneumatophores or colour-changing cells. The dorsal mantle is fused to the head between the eyes, and there are eight tentacles with eight suckers in transverse rows.

3 **COMMON SQUID, INK FISH** or **CALAMARI**
Loligo forbesii
Growing to over 75cm (2.5ft) in length, this is the most common squid in the North Sea. The species inhabits the water column to all depths, feeding on fishes of various species. It comes to shallow depths to lay its gelatinous strings of eggs, attaching them to the sea floor, rocks or kelp stypes. The female lays about 20,000 eggs in one session, usually around the time of the full moon from June to October. This squid is a commercially important species and is caught by trawl nets or with night lights and jigs.

4 **LESSER** or **CURLED OCTOPUS**
Eledone cirrhosa
Although this is known as the Lesser Octopus in the North Sea, it is so numerous in northern waters that it is regarded as the common or only octopus. It commonly grows to over 45cm (18in) in length, and its eight tentacles are slender and taper to a blunt point. They have a single row of suckers and a wide spread. The body is rather soft and sac-like, and either warty or smooth (depending on its mood). It is usually reddish-brown to mottled brown and cream, with the colour being lighter below. Found in deeper rockpools on the lower shore, it is considered a pest in areas of commercial lobstering, as it will enter lobster pots and eat the lobsters before fishermen have time to empty the pots.

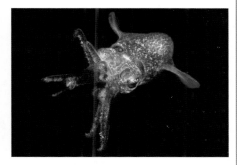

1 Common Cuttlefish
(*above*)
2 Little Cuttlefish
(*above right*)

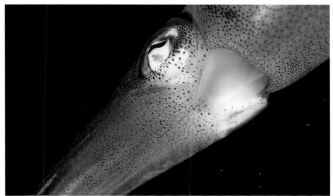

3 Common Squid (*right*)
4 Lesser Octopus (*below*)

SNAILS (GASTROPODS)

Gastropods comprise the largest class of the Mollusca family and their body form is widely varied. They include all univalved shellfish such as chitons, limpets, periwinkles and snails. Usually equipped with a shell of one piece, they live mostly on the shore, in seaweeds or on the sea bottom. The group also includes bivalves, shells and animals with two shells, often equal in size, such as scallops and mussels, as well as sea slugs or nudibranchs, which have no shell at all and respire through external gills.

CHITONS

1 MULTICOLOURED CHITON
Tonicella rubra
The name says it all! This common chiton is quite long and oval, with a wide range of colours on both the dorsal plates and the mantle. It grows to only 20mm (¾in) in length and has the characteristic eight plates. Its habitat is calcareous algae, which give it its distinctive colour. It is found on the shore and sub-tidally from Iceland and northern Norway to Denmark and south to the Bay of Biscay.

2 RED CHITON
Tonicella marmorea
A deep red coloration is characteristic of this large chiton, which can grow to up to 40mm (1½in) in length and is quite round and ovoid in shape. Its girdle is narrow and uniform in colour, with the plates being rather rough to the touch. Most commonly inhabiting northern European shores, the Red Chiton prefers a relatively shaded environment and is often found under stones or in recesses.

3 BROWN CHITON
Acanthochitona crinitus
This chiton is flattened and rather elongate, and generally a rather drab brown in colour. It usually grows to about 2.5cm (1in) in length. The dorsal shell comprises eight interlocking transverse plates, and the edge of the girdle has 18 tufts of long hairs. The Brown Chiton is found on the lower shore throughout the North Sea region, where it lives among barnacles, small crustose algae and anemones.

LIMPETS

4 BLUE-RAYED LIMPET
Helcion pellucidum
This is a beautiful small limpet with iridescent bands and spots of brilliant blue across an almost translucent amber shell, which radiate from the apex of the shell. The blue bands fade as a limpet gets older. Living almost exclusively on various types of kelp, the Blue-rayed Limpet excavates holes in the algae and feeds to its heart's content. Its maximum size is only around 15mm (½in).

5 COMMON LIMPET
Patella vulgata
The most common limpet exposed on the seashore, this species has a very robust shell that may be covered in fine calcareous or other types of seaweed. The shell can be as large as 5cm (2in) in length and is roughly cylindrical to oval in shape. Where algae do not obscure the outer surface, the growth lines are visible as raised ridges. The Common Limpet is found on the lower shore throughout the range of the North Sea and south into the Bay of Biscay.

6 TORTOISESHELL LIMPET
Tectura testudinalis
This species is very similar to the Common Limpet, *Patella vulgata*, but normally only grows to 25mm (1in) in diameter. Roughly cylindrical in shape, but with a more grooved margin, the shell of the Tortoiseshell Limpet is smoothly ridged and has brilliant tortoiseshell markings throughout. Whenever these shells are washed up on the seashore, they are very fine and almost translucent.

7 SMOOTH TORTOISESHELL LIMPET
Acmaea virginea
This is a similar species to the Tortoiseshell Limpet, *Tectura testudinalis*, but it prefers depths of 6m (20ft) or more and overall has a much smoother shell, with a clearly defined oval shape to the perimeter. It has characteristic pale broad stripes that are more evident at the edges.

1 Multicoloured Chiton

2 Red Chiton

3 Brown Chiton

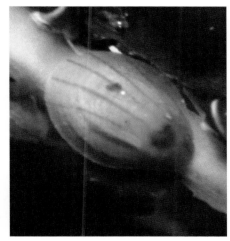

4 Blue-rayed Limpet

5 Common Limpet

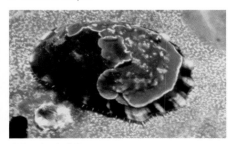

6 Tortoiseshell Limpet

7 Smooth Tortoiseshell Limpet

TOPSHELLS

1 **PAINTED TOPSHELL**
Calliostoma zizyphinum
The Painted Topshell has a very distinctively shaped shell, conical in shape with about 12 flattened whorls rising to a pointed apex. Usually reddish-brown with yellow and cream blotches all over, it is always covered in calcareous algae. It prefers a deeper habitat below 9m (30ft), and appears to favour a tidal location, where it feeds on various algae and sessile invertebrates such as bryozoans. The Painted Topshell is distributed throughout the North Sea and extends as far as the Azores and Canary Islands.

2 **GREY TOPSHELL**
Gibbula cineraria
Rarely grey in colour despite its name, the shell of this topshell is more of a mauve colour and grows to 1.5cm (¾in) in height. It has a rather blunt apex and is fairly smooth in profile, but not so smooth that various algae will not make their home on its back. It is found on the lower shore, feeds on algae and is quite at home in deeper rockpools. When the outer shell of the Grey Topshell is chipped it reveals a brilliant mother-of-pearl layer.

WHELKS & WINKLES

3 **EDIBLE WINKLE** or **COMMON PERIWINKLE**
Littorina littorea
The coloration of the Edible Winkle may vary, but it is generally dull grey-green to black and brown, and it grows to 25mm (1in) tall. Conical in shape, it is associated with barnacles and wracks on the shore. The growth lines are much more obvious in juveniles than in adults, and in young winkles the tentacled eye-stalks are banded. The shell of this species is one of the most common littoral shells found around all the shores of the North Sea, on all rocky coasts except for the most exposed locatons. The Edible Winkle is tolerant of varied salinity

and can also be found on estuarine mud flats. It is highly prized for the seafood market.

4 **FLAT PERIWINKLE**
Littorina obtusata
This species has a flat-topped shell and is commonly seen throughout the North Sea feeding exclusively on various wracks. It occurs in many different colours, from orange, olive-green and red to various shades of brown. It can withstand large changes of temperature and water salinity, and the empty shells are often found washed up on beaches after storms.

5 **BANDED CINGULA**
Cingula cingillus
The Banded Cingula's tiny shell is found in small aggregations under stones and on various kelps and wracks. It feeds on the Sea Mat, *Membranipora membranacea*, living on kelp, and is seen on the leading edges of this encrusting bryozoan. The shell is pale fawn or cream in colour with a brown stripe running up the spire, which has about four whorls. It grows to a maximum length of only about 5mm (¼in).

6 **BANDED CHINK SHELL**
Lacuna vincta
This species has a small shell very similar to that of the Banded Cingula, *Cingula cingillus*, with a low spire, and is found on a number of algae including *Halydris*. Usually orange to amber in colour with brown or white spiral lines around the four whorls, it is quite small, only growing to 12mm (½in) in length. Preferring deeper water, it is most commonly found sub-tidally in depths of over 6m (20ft).

7 **NETTED DOG WHELK**
Nassarius reticulatus
With a shell growing to about 25mm (1in) long, the Netted Dog Whelk is a scavenger. Using their incredible sensory apparatus, large numbers of this whelk will find the corpse of a fish or some other creature. When crawling along, the whelk's siphon is held high above its head. The shell is rather rough and a drab greyish-brown in colour with deeply sculpted patterns.

1 Painted Topshell

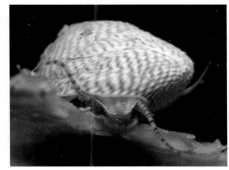

2 Grey Topshell

3 Edible Winkle

4 Flat Periwinkle

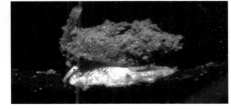

5 Banded Cingula (*above*)
6 Banded Chink Shell (*above right*)
7 Netted Dog Whelk (*right*)

1 DOG WHELK
Nucella lapillus
The Dog Whelk has quite a heavy, thick shell with a very sharp spire and usually about five rough whorls. It can grow to as large as 4cm (1½in) in length, but is usually much smaller. Pale cream in colour turning to brown at the end of the spire, it is commonly found around all shores and feeds on barnacles, mussels and calcareous algae. It lays pale yellow egg capsules, usually on the undersides of rocks, during early spring.

2 EDIBLE WHELK or BUCKIE
Buccinum undatum
This is a large whelk that is up to 10cm (4in) high and 5cm (2in) wide, with 7–8 whorls with spiral ridges. The shell colour is usually yellowish-brown with blotched lighter markings on the spire. The aperture is quite broad and oval, and tapers to a point, which has a short, wide siphonal canal. The mantle of the snail is white with black blotches, and it has a long, upturned siphon. It lays clumps of creamy-yellow eggs, which may form a column 10cm (4in) high and 7.5cm (3in) in diameter. This whelk is a highly sought-after food species and is found on many seafood restaurant menus.

3 PELICAN'S-FOOT SHELL
Aporrhais pespelicani
The shell of this snail is quite wide at around 2.4cm (1in), generally spindle-shaped with a well-developed sculpture and about ten whorls, and pale cream in colour. The aperture is long, irregularly formed and with distinct splits, and the shell forms four or five blunt tips that look similar to the splayed foot of a pelican or other seabird (hence the name). The mouth is long and drawn-out, with two rows of radula (or rasping plates), each of which has seven teeth, and a short siphon. The snail lives in muddy or fine sand sediments.

4 NECKLACE SHELL
Euspira catena
This snail has a glossy, rounded shell and grows to about 35mm (1½in). It has a very broad foot that extends some way beyond the shell and

envelops the lower margins, and two prominent-tentacled and fairly obvious black eyes. Living on fine sand, it preys upon small bivalves that live below the sand. It lays a characteristic band of eggs, cemented together with sand particles. This looks like a fringed belt forming an open circle and resembles a necklace (hence the snail's common name).

5 TURRET, AUGER or TOWER SHELL
Turritella communis
This snail has a long, sharply pointed shell made up of about 20 whorls, and will reach 5cm (2in). The rounded shell aperture is quite small and is rarely if ever seen, as the snail is very sluggish in motivation and sits with its head buried in a muddy substrate, where it sifts mud and sea water for food particles. The shell of the species is always partly exposed, and it can form large colonies. It is often associated with the Turret Shell Anemone, *Sagartiogeten laceratus*.

6 EUROPEAN or SPOTTED COWRIE
Trivia monacha
The European Cowrie is a marine mollusc that has an egg-shaped, glossy shell featuring many transverse ridges and a long, narrow aperture on the underside. It grows to around 15mm (⅝in) and feeds on soft bryozoans and hydroids. The upper surface of the shell is usually reddish-brown in colour, and has three typical spots that allow the species to be identified easily. The head, tentacles, foot and body are brightly coloured: they may be red, yellow, green, brown or orange.

7 ARCTIC COWRIE
Trivia arctica
Although it is very similar to the European Cowrie, *T. monacha*, the shell of this cowrie is smaller at about 10mm (⅜in), and white in colour with no markings. The mantle of the snail is orange to light brown in colour and usually blotched or striped. It can completely cover the ridged shell. The Arctic Cowrie is most regularly found in the northern waters of the North Sea, around Scotland and Scandinavia.

1 Dog Whelk

2 Edible Whelk

3 Pelican's-foot Shell

4 Necklace Shell

5 Turret Shell

6 European Cowie

7 Arctic Cowie

BIVALVES

1 POD RAZOR or SPOUT
Ensis siliqua
This is a burrowing bivalve that grows to about 20cm (8in). It has an elongated, fragile and narrow shell shaped like a cut-throat razor, hence the common name. The two halves of the shell, known as valves, are straight sided. They have a smooth, whitish outer surface with reddish or purplish-brown markings, and are covered by an olive-green layer of protein known as the periostracum. The inner surface of the valves is white with a purple hue. The large, muscular foot is reddish-brown in colour and is considered highly desirable in European food markets. The species is relatively common throughout the North Sea region and has several similarly shaped relatives.

2 FLAME SHELL
Limaria hians
As the name of the Flame Shell suggests, the edge of its fleshy mantle bears numerous conspicuous, red and orange filamentous tentacles. The shell is thin and solid with two equal valves, and generally oval-shaped. It grows to about 2.5cm (1in), but can be larger. The shell is white in young individuals, becoming whitish-brown with age, and has clearly defined growth lines and around 50 radiating ribs. When it is disturbed, this species can swim actively using jets of water expelled by 'clapping' its shells together (similar to scallops) and a rowing motion with its tentacles. It is known to build mat-like nests in Maerle and other similar substrates, producing sticky thread to bind stones and shells together for the nests. Most commonly found in the Western Isles and sea lochs of Scotland, it also occurs along the Norwegian coast and a few areas in Denmark.

3 COCKLE
Cerastoderma edule
The familiarly shaped edible Cockle has a thick shell that is quite solid, with both halves or valves of equal size, growing to a maximum of around 5cm (2in), but generally half that size. It favours a sublittoral environment in muddy sand, into which it burrows shallowly. The shell has 22–28 radiating ribs crossed by conspicuous concentric ridges, and may bear short, flat spines. It is off-white in colour or slightly tinged with yellow or orange-brown, depending on the substrate it is on. This is an important food species and is commercially harvested in many areas.

4 SAND GAPER
Mya arenaria
This clam has a robust white shell that can grow to 150mm (6in) in length. Both ends of the shell are characteristically rounded in formation. All that divers generally see of this animal is the respiratory siphons protruding above the sand. It is widely distributed from France to the Arctic.

5 QUEEN SCALLOP or QUEENIE
Aequipecten opercularis
This small scallop is highly prized in the seafood market and is harvested throughout the North Sea region. It grows to about 9cm (3½in) in diameter and has 20 sculpted, bold ridges on each side. Highly mobile when danger threatens, it moves by pumping the muscular joint within the shell, creating a jerky locomotion. Both sides of this bivalve are curved, but there is a definite top and bottom. The top is usually covered in the encrusting Scallop Sponge, *Pseudosuberites sulphereus*.

6 GREAT SCALLOP
Pecten maximus
A large, commercially important species, the Great Scallop is harvested relentlessly for the growing food markets of Europe, and is highly prized. Its shell has two equal-sized valves, but the top is flat and the underside is curved; both valves have deeply radiating ribs and grow to about 15cm (6in) in diameter. The fleshy mantle at the top and bottom has many small tentacles and tiny eye-spots. The scallop is found slightly sunk into the seabed, which is usually fine sand and gravel, but may also be mud. It is a filter feeder and sits with its valves open. To escape from danger the Great Scallop may rapidly pulse its central muscle, causing the shells to flap together and creating propulsion; it does, however, tire quickly and soon drops back down to the seabed.

1 Pod Razor

2 Flame Shell

3 Cockle

4 Sand Gaper

5 Queen Scallop (*above*)

6 Great Scallop (*right*)

1 COMMON MUSSEL
Mytilus edulis

Located extensively in shallow water, especially around the surf zone, Common Mussels are a highly prized food species that is commercially raised for the food market in many areas. They have equally shaped and sized valves, are dark bluish-purple in colour and are able to attach themselves together in large groups by means of renewable byssus or stiff secreted thread. They grow to up to 5cm (2in) long.

2 HORSE MUSSEL
Modiolus modiolus

A cousin of the Common Mussel, *Mytilus edulis*, this species is much larger in size, growing to over 15cm (6in) in length. It prefers a far deeper habitat and lives on rough ground in sand, mud, gravel, small stones and rocks. The valves are equally rounded and generally rhomboidal in shape. Horse Mussels form dense beds on the sea floor and are usually covered in calcareous algae, other seaweeds, hydroids and bryozoans.

3 RIBBED SADDLE OYSTER
Pododesmus patelliformis

As its name implies, this mollusc is something of an anomaly. It has two halves, and the lower part is an almost translucent mother-of-pearl and is cemented to the substratum. The upper part is shaped like a flat limpet, slightly ribbed and can be opened by means of a muscular foot. These oysters are very hard to find because they are usually adhered flat to the rock and covered in bits of algae, hydroids or crud. They grow to about 5cm (2in), but are usually half this size.

SEA HARES & SEA SLUGS (NUDIBRANCHS)

Members of the Opisthobranch superfamily, sea hares have large, fleshy bodies with lobed sensory and oral tentacles. When disturbed they can eject a purple dye and milky-white sticky threads as a means of defence. They have internal shells. Sea slugs, on the other hand, are snails that have lost their shells.

The name nudibranch literally means 'naked gills'. Nudibranchs are a wide and diverse group with many differing body forms, but all species share the same characteristics. They have two long sensory organs at the head called rhinophores, various tubercles or tentacles across the body and a set of external breathing gills, dorsally and near the rear of the body. They are carnivores, and most have the ability to store the stinging nematocysts from the hydroids that they have eaten as a means of additional defence. Many are very colourful.

4 SEA HARE
Aplysia punctata

Growing to up to around 20cm (8in), the Sea Hare is usually at least half this size, with its coloration depending on the algae it is eating. It is usually from brown to deep red in colour, delicately marked with lighter spots over a mottled or blotched body. It is generally found in deeper rockpools and sublittorally.

5 BERTHELLA
Bertella plumula

This species is actually a member of the Pleurobranchia and is a bridge between the true nudibranchs and gastropod snails. Outwardly it looks like a small, rounded dorid nudibranch with its gills retracted, but this species has an internal shell. The shell is transparent and about half its body length, which may reach 50mm (2in). It is usually bright orange in colour, and is able to protect itself by secreting sulphuric acid if it is attacked. The species is fairly common around all shores of the North Sea, and extends from Norway down to the Mediterranean.

6 SOFT CORAL SLUG
Tritonia hombergi

Typically white, or pale cream as juveniles and cream with mottled brown as adults, this nudibranch is the main feeder on Dead Man's Fingers, *Alcyonium digitatum*, soft corals. It is one of the few species that is able to live through two growing seasons, and its size in year one is typically up to about 5cm (2in), while in year two it can grow to over 20cm (8in). There are rows of tufts along the sides of its mantle and two prominent rhinophores, and its back is also covered in tubercles. It lays large streamers of pinkish-brown eggs on or near the soft coral host.

1 Common Mussel

2 Horse Mussel

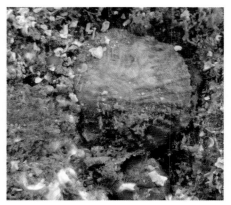

3 Ribbed Saddle Oyster

4 Sea Hare

5 Berthella

6 Soft Coral Slug

1 LINED TRITONIA
Tritonia lineate
A cousin of the Soft Coral Slug, *T. hombergi*, this nudibranch grows to only about 2.5cm (1in) in length. Its body is an opaque, pale bluish-white with two very distinct white lines that pass from head to narrow-pointed tail on either side and rise up to each small tuft of 4–6 pairs of arborescent gill tufts on its back. It can be found in most regions and feeds on bryozoans and hydroids.

2 FROND NUDIBRANCH
Dendronotus frondosus
There are at least four very distinct colour variations of this large sea slug: orange-mottled red, white, mottled red and orange with a row of white spots down the back and pinkish all over with a darker red line down the back. The species has nine pairs of cerata and large branched rhinophores. It can grow to over 7.5cm (3in) and feeds on the Hairy Sea Mat, *Electra pilosa*, which encrusts various seaweeds below depths of 6m (20ft).

3 NODE DORIS
Goniodoris nodosa
The Node Doris is a soft-bodied but quite plump nudibranch that is elongate in nature with a pronounced skirt around the edge of the mantle. It grows to over 2.5cm (1in) in length, but is more commonly much less than that. Its rhinophores are tinged yellow and flattened, and it has small, pointed oral tentacles. At the rear of the animal there is a rosette of 13 branched gills. The Node Doris is known from the Faero Islands, southern Norway, Denmark and south to Spain.

4 *Onchidoris luteocincta*
Growing to around 2.5cm (1in) in length, this nudibranch is easily distinguished from many others by the distinctive colour markings along its back and margins. The centre of its back is brick-red in colour fading to white, and its brilliant yellow fringe is also lined in white. Its back is covered in large, white, spiky tubercles, and it has two long, white, spiral rhinophores. This species eats bryozoans and is only found subtidally, usually below 6m (20ft).

5 *Limacea clavigera*
This easily recognized, yet small nudibranch grows to around 2cm (¾in) in length. It is white in colour and has a stout fringed mantle; all of its rhinophores, tentacles and various tubercles are tipped with brilliant yellow. It has a number of extended tentacles at the front of the head, which also extends below the margin. The species is common throughout the North Sea and feeds on a variety of bryozoans.

6 FOUR-LINED NUDIBRANCH
Polycera quadrilineata
This nudibranch is very common throughout the North Sea, feeding on sea mat that encrusts various kelp seaweeds. It has a distinct white body with yellow stripes around the frame, and may have lots of black and yellow spots on the flanks. It has four prominent, yellow-tipped oral tentacles, two large, yellow-tipped rhinophores and yellow-tinged gills. The Four-lined Nudibranch grows to about 3.5cm (1½in) in length.

7 NORTHERN POLYCERA
Polycera faeroensis
The Northern Polycera is similar to the Four-lined Nudibranch, *P. quadrilineata*, but more uniform in both colour and markings. It grows to 4.5cm (1.8in) in length, and has a translucent white body with yellow tips to its tentacles, rhinophores and gills. Where the Four-lined Nudibranch has four tentacles around the mouth, the Northern Polycera has around ten and also has a much broader head.

1 Lined Tritonia

2 Frond Nudibranch

3 Node Doris

4 *Onchidoris luteocincta*

5 *Limacea clavigera*

6 Four-lined Nudibranch

7 Northern Polycera

1 YELLOW-TIPPED NUDIBRANCH
Ancula gibbosa
On first appearance this species is quite similar to the Four-lined Nudibranch, *Polycera quadrilineata*: it also has four brilliant-yellow-tipped tentacles under its white rhinophores, but it additionally has 3–4 yellow-tipped tentacles in two rows on either side of its white gills. The Yellow-tipped Nudibranch grows to about 2.5cm (1in) in length and is most commonly found on a rocky substrate, where it feeds on bryozoans and hydroids.

2 WHITE-LINED NUDIBRANCH
Coryphella lineata
This species grows to up to 5cm (2in) in length and has seven paired clusters of cerata, all of which are white-tipped. The body colour is various shades of brown, and it has a distinctive lateral line from the tail to the head along the centre of the back. It feeds on various hydroids and bryozoans, and is common throughout the North Sea.

3 *Facelina bostoniensis*
There are quite a few species in the *Facelina* genus. Most of them are very similar in appearance and it is usually not possible to identify them without a microscopic examination. *F. bostoniensis*, however, is characterized by having a vivid dark red or maroon patch behind and between the rhinophores at the back of its head.

4 PURPLE NUDIBRANCH
Flabellina pedata
This distinctively coloured nudibranch has a purple body and white tips to all its cerata. Its tentacles grow to approximately 50mm (2in) in length. Its rhinophores have a distinctly wrinkled surface and are purple in colour, although this may vary between individuals.

Purple Nudibranchs may be found feeding on various hydroids, and are common throughout the North Sea region.

5 CORONET NUDIBRANCH
Facelina coronata
This sea slug has a body around 4cm (1½in) in length. Two pairs of tentacles are attached to its head, which has very long rhinophores. The body is translucent white and the red oesophagus can be seen through the skin of the head. There are six groups of cerata with multiple tentacles along the back, usually coloured pinkish-red with white tips. The species is found throughout the British Isles, Scandinavia and other parts of northern Europe.

6 COMMON GREY SEA SLUG
Aeolidia papillosa
The body of this large sea slug is a mottled grey-brown in colour, and most of it is covered by soft, white-tipped cerata arranged in 25 closely packed crowns; only its mid-back is clean of any tentacles. There are two pairs of tentacles and long rhinophores on the head. It feeds on small anemones and hydroids. This sea slug grows to around 10cm (4in) in length and is distributed from Iceland to the western Mediterranean.

7 CRYSTAL TIPS
Janolus cristatus
The Crystal Tips is about 7.5cm (3in) in length and has an oval, flattened shape. Its body is fringed all around by golden cerata or tentacles, each of which is tipped with white and iridescent blue. The rhinophores are white and non-retractile. Widely distributed in the North Sea region, this species is an active night-time predator, feeding on bryozoans. Crystal Tips can be found on many different substrates, preferring clean, shallow and sheltered waters.

1 Yellow-tipped Nudibranch

2 White-lined Nudibranch

4 Purple Nudibranch

3 *Facelina bostoniensis*

5 Coronet Nudibranch (*right*)

6 Common Grey Sea Slug (*above*)

7 Crystal Tips (*right*)

1 SEA LEMON AND EGGS
Archidoris pseudoargus
One of the most common nudibranchs of the Dorid family, this species is found around all the shores of the North Sea. Usually a mottled lemon yellow or orange in colour, it is covered in warty tubercles similar to those found on a lemon (hence its name). It lays a distinctive egg collar, which is also yellowish in colour. The species prefers a sub-tidal position, but is occasionally found in rockpools. It can grow to 5cm (2in) in length.

2 BROWN DORIS
Onchidoris fusca
A common small nudibranch, the Brown Doris is extremely communal in its habits and is often found in large breeding aggregations amid coils of its white eggs. It is generally mottled brown in colour, oval in shape and only 12mm (½in) long. Its food consists of small sponges and bryozoans.

3 Adalaria proxima
The body of this species is usually off-white in colour, and its mantle is covered by rounded tubercles with conical tips. Its rhinophores are generally darker in appearance than the rest of the mantle, and it grows to about 18mm (¾in) in length. It is mostly found feeding on the Hairy Sea Mat, *Electra pilosa*, but is quite at home on a number of encrusting bryozoans.

4 FUZZY DORIS
Acanthodoris pilosa
This nudibranch is very similar in appearance to *Adalaria proxima*, but where this species' tubercles are rounded or have rounded points, the Fuzzy Doris, as its name suggests, has an overall 'fuzzy' appearance due to the tubercles being positioned much closer together and having pointed tips. Overall white to pale grey in colour, it grows to about 50mm (2in) in length and feeds on various bryozoans, including the Horned Wrack, *Fucus ceranoides*.

5 Cuthona concinna
This is a small nudibranch that grows to 2cm (¾in) in length. It is pale cream in colour, with two white-pointed tentacles located between a rounded head and two pale rhinophores. The body has 14–16 tentacles along each side of the dorsal margin. *C. concinna* is a shallow-water species and is frequently found in rockpools.

6 Doto pinnatifida
This is a curiously shaped, small nudibranch found almost exclusively on *Nermertesia* spp., where it lays its egg whorls. At only 6mm (¼in) long, it is difficult to see and it is the egg whorls that give away its presence. The species has two rows of 7–8 groups of tentacles arranged like 'clubs', and is a dull, mottled orange-brown in colour.

7 Doto coronata
There are a number of very closely related species of *Doto* – among them *D. pinnatifida* and *D. coronata* – that share the characteristics of red pigment spots on the tips of the ceratal tubercles and red pigment along the back, with additional maroon pigment spots or streaks on the body. *D. coronata* has fairly smooth rhinophores that have sheaths with dilated margins. It grows to a maximum size of about 12mm (½in) in length.

8 Eubranchus farrani
E. farrani is variable in colour, but most commonly has a relatively translucent body that has yellow- or orange-tipped tentacles. Juveniles of the species may have no colour other than pale brown or salmon pink. There are no fewer than ten diagonal rows of up to five cerata in each row along the back of this species. These are usually inflated with sea water, making the animal appear much larger than its 18mm (¾in) length. The oral tentacles and rhinophores are similar in size and relatively short.

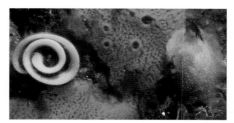

1 Sea Lemon and Eggs

2 Brown Doris

3 *Adalaria proxima*

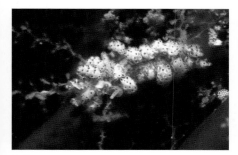

4 Fuzzy Doris

5 *Cuthona concinna*

6 *Doto pinnatifida*

7 *Doto coronata*

8 *Eubranchus farrani*

ECHINODERMS
(FAMILY ECHINODERMATA)

This important phylum is entirely marine in origin and contains many different family groups. Completely varied in form, they nevertheless have common characteristics such as calcareous plates, a water vascular system and tiny tube feet for locomotion and capturing food. Many are armed with some degree of protection. Most obvious of all are the sea urchins, which are surrounded by sharp spines. The family includes the brittlestars, true starfishes, crinoids, sea urchins and sea cucumbers.

BRITTLESTARS

1 BLACK BRITTLESTAR
Ophiocomino nigra
Fairly common in deeper water and not always black in colour as the name suggests, this brittlestar has five arms and five to seven rows of short spines along each arm. Its arms are up to 10cm (4in) long. It feeds on detritus deposits, is omnivorous and can occur in large numbers.

2 FRAGILE BRITTLESTAR
Ophiothrix fragilis
The disc and arms of this colourful species can be of almost any colour imaginable, varying on individuals. Hairy in appearance, the arms, which grow to 6.3cm (2½in) long, are characterized by having numerous rows of relatively long spines. Fragile Brittlestars occur in extremely dense beds in well-aerated, deep water.

3 MUDDY BRITTLESTAR
Ophiura albida
This is a small brittlestar with five short, tapered, straight arms, each 5cm (2in) long. The body and arms are pale reddish-brown in colour, and there are two white marks at the base of each arm where it joins the central body disc. The species prefers a muddy substrate and is found throughout the North Sea region.

CRINOIDS

4 FEATHER STARFISH
Antedon bifida
The most common of the feather stars or crinoids in the region, the Feather Starfish has ten arms with side branches like a feather. It is generally coloured in various deep reds and browns, and its arms are about 5cm (2in) long. It has a disc-like central plate and 25 cirri or modified feet. Usually found in exposed regions, it attaches itself to rock faces and shipwrecks.

5 100-LEGGED CRINOID
Antedon petasus
This is very similar to the Feather Starfish, *A. bifida*, but for one striking difference. Whereas *A. bifida* has 25 cirri, *A. petasus*, as its name suggests, can have as many as 100. The cirri are also longer than in *A. bifida*. The species is found principally in northern regions of the North Sea around the British Isles and Scandinavia.

6 MEDUSA BASKET STAR
Gorgonocephalus caputmedusae
This is a rare deep-water and cold-water species of basket starfish. It is relatively large, with a big central base and long, branching arms, and is usually pale cream or buff in colour. Distributed primarily in the deeper Norwegian fjords and north into the Arctic, it is found across the latitudes to Greenland and Newfoundland.

OTHER STARFISHES

7 BURROWING STARFISH
Astropecten irregularis
This rigid, buff-coloured, star-shaped starfish with five short, tapering arms grows to about 15cm (6in) across and has conspicuous spines along the margin of each arm. It is usually found on clean sand, where it buries itself during the day and comes out at dusk to feed.

1 Black Brittlestar

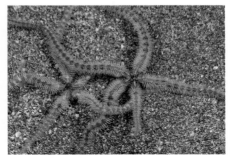

2 Fragile Brittlestar

3 Muddy Brittlestar
(*above*)
4 Feather Starfish
(*below*)

5 100-legged Crinoid
(*above right*)
6 Medusa Basket Star
(*right*)

7 Burrowing Starfish

1 SEVEN-ARMED STARFISH
Luidia ciliaris

This starfish normally has seven arms and is pale orange-brown in colour. It has a conspicuous band of white spines along the underside of each arm and very long tube feet that enable it to move quite fast in its quest for its main food species, brittlestars. The Seven-armed Starfish can grow to up to 40cm (15½in) across and is found on scoured rock faces, gravel and mixed sediments throughout the North Sea area.

2 RED CUSHION STAR
Porania pulvillus

The Red Cushion Star is a very smooth red or orange-red starfish with white, soft papulae over its back. Growing to approximately 12.5cm (5in) across, it has five short arms that blend into the large, rounded central disc. The Red Cushion Star occurs in a variety of habitats, including rocky regions, shipwrecks, exposed shoreline and very deep water. It is most frequently found in the northern regions of the North Sea.

3 YELLOW SUNSTAR
Solaster endeca

A multi-limbed starfish with nine or ten arms, the Yellow Sunstar has a very rough surface combined with a relatively soft body. It resembles a larger, multi-limbed version of the Common Starfish, *Asterias rubens*. The colour of the Yellow Sunstar varies from a muddy cream to pink and purple. It is an active feeder on brittlestars, and can grow to more than 40cm (16in) in diameter.

4 COMMON or RED SUNSTAR
Crossaster papposus

The Common Sunstar is a large, circular starfish that usually has 13 arms. It is always a brilliant colour of shades varying from red to orange and purple, with two lighter rings located around the base and midway along each arm. It inhabits tidal streams and is found in relatively exposed sites at depths of below 15m (60ft). The Common Sunstar is most often found in northern waters.

5 NORTHERN HENRICIA or BLOODY HENRY
Henricia sanguinolenta

A rather stiff and rigid starfish with five tapering arms and a very rough texture, the Northern Henricia grows to around 12.5cm (5in) across and is usually pink-purple in colour, although it can be anything from vivid red to purple. It lives in a variety of habitats and feeds on hydroids and bryozoans.

6 COMMON STARFISH
Asterias rubens

This is the most common of all the starfishes and the one that is most likely to be see on the foreshore. It has a rather hard skin, but is relatively soft and floppy, rough in texture and usually pale brown or mauve. There is a line of paler white tubercles down the centre of each arm and numerous tubercles. The Common Starfish is an active feeder on detritus and is one of the few echinoderms that can tolerate brackish water.

7 SPINY STARFISH
Marthasterias glacialis

One of the largest starfishes found in the North Sea, the Spiny Starfish has five very long, sub-cylindrical arms that are roughly tapering and covered in longitudinal rows of thick, sharp spines. Each spine is surrounded by a raised group of pedicellariae. The species prefers rocky substrate and is mottled green-brown in colour. It grows to over 70cm (2.3ft) in diameter.

SEA URCHINS

8 COMMON SEA URCHIN
Echinus esculentus

This is a large, globular, colourful sea urchin that grows to over 17.5cm (7in) in diameter. It has short white spines and long tube feet, and the rest of it is usually coloured in variations of red and orange. An algae grazer, in some areas it has denuded entire rock surfaces of all large algae. It is collected for the curio trade, and in some European countries the pale yellow gonads are eaten as a delicacy.

1 Seven-armed Starfish

2 Red Cushion Star

4 Common Sunstar

3 Yellow Sunstar

5 Northern
Henricia
(*above*)
6 Common
Starfish
(*above left*)
7 Spiny
Starfish (*left*)
8 Common
Sea Urchin
(*right*)

1 NORTHERN SEA URCHIN
Psammechinus miliaris
This small, slightly flattened sea urchin only grows to a maximum of 5cm (2in) in diameter. The shell is greenish, and the spines are tinged purple or have violet tips. The species prefers areas of low light and shallow water, where it hides under stones or among seagrasses or seaweeds. It is widely distributed from Iceland to Norway and the Baltic.

2 PURPLE HEART URCHIN
Spatangus purpureus
As its name suggests, the Purple Heart Urchin is indeed heart shaped and coloured a brilliant purple, with light, fine spines. It can grow to as large as 12cm (4¾in) across and only burrows shallowly, preferring coarse sand and shell gravel. The Purple Heart Urchin is found in all areas of the North Sea and northern Europe, as well as in the Mediterranean.

3 COMMON HEART URCHIN or SEA POTATO
Echinocardium cordatum
The common name of this urchin refers to the brittle, empty shell or test, which is sometimes seen on the sandy seabed or shore. When alive, the animal is covered in a mat of fine, cream spines almost like hairs. Slightly heart-shaped, fairly round and up to 7.5cm (3in) across, it burrows in the fine sand and is a deposit feeder.

SEA CUCUMBERS

4 BURROWING SEA CUCUMBER
Neopendactyla mixta
One of the most common burrowing sea cucumbers, this species can be seen with its fringe of tentacles rising above a sand and gravel seabed. Often white in colour or flecked with cream and brown, it has five rows of tube feet and three rings of ten tentacles that vary in size. The Burrowing Sea Cucumber is often associated with Horse Mussel beds and is found throughout the northern North Sea.

5 RED BURROWING CUCUMBER
Psolus phantapus
This is one of the more exotically coloured burrowing sea cucumbers, with an off-white body covered in orange blotches and pink spots. Growing to up to 20cm (8in) in length, the body is U-shaped and has a sole at the base, where the tube feet are confined. The species prefers a muddy or mud and gravel substrate, and most of it is usually on show.

6 *Thyone fusus*
Quite similar in appearance to the Burrowing Sea Cucumber, *Neopendactyla mixta*, this burrowing sea cucumber also lies partly buried in soft sand and gravel and raises its fringe net of tentacles into the current to feed. The body and tentacles are brown, and the body is sometimes covered in shell or sand particles. Growing to around 20cm (8in) in length, it has ten widely branched tentacles. The species is usually found in depths below 15m (50ft), and apparently also favours the company of mussels.

7 *Aslia lefevrei*
This species has a brown, leathery body and ten dark brown, mottled tentacles that form a net of branches. Like *Pawsoni saxicola*, it has five rows of tube feet and grows to 15cm (6in) in length, with tentacles 10cm (4in) long. It lives in rocky crevices from the lower shore down to 30m (100ft), and is found in all northern regions of the North Sea.

8 *Pawsonia saxicola*
This sea cucumber has a white, smooth skin on the body and a fringe of dark, blotched tentacles. It has five distinct rows of tube feet and grows to around 15cm (6in) in length, with tentacles a further 10cm (4in) long. It lives in rocky crevices, sometimes under boulders, where it abuts the gravel and sand.

1 Northern Sea Urchin

2 Purple Heart Urchin

3 Common Heart Urchin

4 Burrowing Sea Cucumber

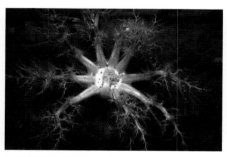

5 Red Burrowing Cucumber

6 *Thyone fusus*

7 *Aslia lefevrei*

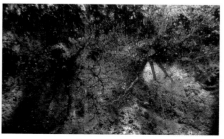

8 *Pawsonia saxicola*

ASCIDIANS OR TUNICATES (SEA SQUIRTS)

There are over 3,000 species worldwide in the family Urochordata or ascidians – more commonly called tunicates or sea squirts. They give the appearance of being very simple animals: they have sack-like bodies, and filter feed through their incurrent and excurrent siphons. Looking similar to attached jellyfishes, they are in fact members of the Chordata phylum (which comprises all vertebrates including humans), since they possess a gut and intestine, as well as a rod-like structure similar to the vertebrate backbone. They are either solitary or occur in large communal groups. Juveniles resemble tadpoles in shape, whereas adults have a barrel-like shape when attached.

Most tunicate species are hermaphroditic. They keep eggs and sperm inside their body cavities until both are released into the sea, where they fertilize. Some species remain in a pelagic state and, while resembling their sedentary cousins, they either swim or drift in the open sea. Tunicates earn their other common name of sea squirts from their habit of ejecting a spray of water when disturbed.

1 COMMON SEA SQUIRT
Ciona intestinalis
Usually found on its own, this sea squirt grows to about 15cm (6in) in length and has a white, translucent body, with lobed ends to its two siphons that are sometimes ringed with yellow. The inhalant opening is on the top and the exhalant opening is about one-third of the way down the body. This species is often found with the similarly sized tunicate *Ascidiella aspersa*. It occurs throughout the North Sea region and is common at all depths, being particularly fond of manmade structures such as piers, shipwrecks and buoys – its wide distribution may be due to its propensity to attach itself to ships' hulls.

2 PINK SEA SQUIRT
Ascidia mentula
This is a solitary ascidian that can grow to as large as 18cm (7in) tall. Its body is elongated and always attached by its left side. Each of its two siphons is small, and the overall colour is smooth pink to slightly green-tinged. The species is found in Norway, southern Sweden, throughout Denmark and the north and west of the British Isles.

3 LIGHT-BULB TUNICATE
Clavelina lepadiformis
This sea squirt grows in small, attached colonies and is around 15mm (½in) tall with distinctive white, light-bulb filament markings within the transparent body cavity. The colonies are quite loose in structure and form small clumps. The zooids are cylindrical and smooth, and you may be able to spot amber- or red-coloured eggs or tadpole-shaped larvae within the body cavity. The Light-bulb Tunicate is sometimes found in deeper rockpools, but is usually associated more with harbour walls, vertical cliffs and ledges.

4 FOOTBALL SEA SQUIRT
Diazone violacea
This species forms a tightly packed group of individuals that resemble the Light-bulb Tunicate, *Clavelina lepadiformis*, in structure. In the case of the Football Sea Squirt, however, a colony is grouped to form a ball shape reaching 20cm (8in) in height and over 40cm (1ft 4in) in diameter.

5 STALKED SEA SQUIRT
Aplidium punctum
This colonial sea squirt forms a cluster of club-shaped lobes at the end of a well-developed stalk, and grows to around 25mm (1in) tall. Although the overall appearance is of an orange-pink colour, each individual is quite transparent with an orange spot. Stalked Sea Squirts favour vertical rock faces, and are always found among various algae, hydroids and bryozoans.

1 Common Sea Squirt

3 Light-bulb Tunicate

2 Pink Sea Squirt

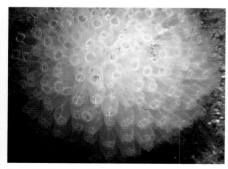

4 Football Sea Squirt

5 Stalked Sea Squirt

1 CLUSTER SEA SQUIRT
Morcellium argus
Very similar in appearance to the Stalked Sea Squirt, *Aplidium punctum*, this stalked and colony-forming species has four spots per zooid. It is club-shaped with a head approximately 25mm (1in) across, and like the Stalked Sea Squirt is found in well-aerated water with strong tidal streams. It occurs in a wide habitat in generally shallow water among many seaweeds and hydroids, and is found in most northern areas of the North Sea.

2 CORELLA
Corella parallelogramma
This is a solitary sea squirt with a squarish-oval body that is generally compressed laterally. It has a basal attachment and two siphons on opposite sides of its body, which is transparent. This allows the gut and pharynx to be clearly seen. Inside there is yellow, white and red pigmentation, often in a criss-cross pattern: these are the body muscles. Nearly rectangular in profile and laterally flattened, the Corella grows to 5cm (2in) in height and is often found in shallow, well-aerated waters. It occurs in a range of habitats – these are always on a hard substratum and all are sublittoral with depths ranging from those of shallow coastal waters to those in excess of 150m (500ft). This sea squirt appears to favour strong tidal movements and surge conditions. It has been recorded in Norway, in all areas of the North Sea, and east in the Baltic Sea and Mediterranean.

3 BAKED-BEAN ASCIDIAN
Dendrodoa grossularia
This small orange or red sea squirt is only about 12mm (½in) in length, and often occurs in dense aggregations. It is commonly associated with a number of hydroids, and often found with the Clathrina Sponge, *Clathrina coriacea* – the white or yellow lacy network of the sponge weaves its way around the sea squirts, making for an amazing colour assault. The species has a globular shape, which may be flattened, and two very obvious but short siphons. The siphons are square or four-lobed when closed, and round and flared when the animal is feeding. The species prefers low light conditions

and is often found in large, well-aerated caverns in all depths of water, including the lower shore, as long as it is fairly sheltered from direct wave action. It grows on rocks, stones, shells, algae and other animals such as ascidians. It is common in all regions of the North Sea except north-east Scotland – although it is found further north in Norwegian and Danish waters.

4 STAR ASCIDIAN
Botryllus schlosseri
This curious ascidian forms flat, encrusting colonies that can extend up kelp stypes or over rocky surfaces. The zooids are elliptical in shape, formed around a common centre with 10–12 individuals and roughly star-shaped in a rounded formation. The colony is generally longer along one axis and golden-yellow in colour, although it does occur in a wide variety of other colours and shapes, sometimes making accurate identification very difficult. This is a common species in all regions of the North Sea, from the lower shore down, and it is usually associated with various kelps and wracks. It is particularly common where there is high wave action and strong current exposure.

5 SEA SQUIRT MAT
Botrylloides leachii
A common, distinctly encrusting colonial sea squirt that forms flat, but thick, fleshy pads, this species occurs in a variety of colours, from yellow, through green and brownish-pink. Its zooids are arranged in irregular lines. It is found on rocky surfaces and large stones, and also encrusts the bases of large kelp plants. The Sea Squirt Mat favours high wave surge and current action, and is relatively common in depths of under 9m (30ft), generally in a hard rock substratum.

6 COLONIAL SEA SQUIRT
Didemnum albidum
The Colonial Sea Squirt forms a thin, pale white to translucent crust over rocky surfaces and larger kelp plant holdfasts. It has characteristic star-shaped oral siphons and forms an irregular shape. The species is found from the intertidal zone to extreme depths in all areas of the North Sea.

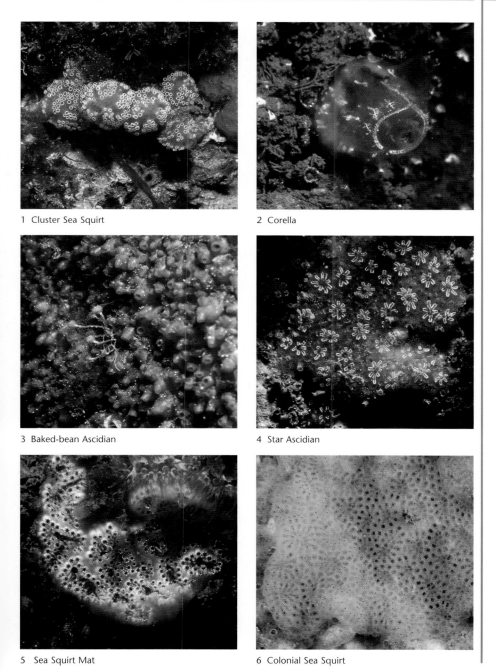

1 Cluster Sea Squirt

2 Corella

3 Baked-bean Ascidian

4 Star Ascidian

5 Sea Squirt Mat

6 Colonial Sea Squirt

CARTILAGINOUS FISHES (SHARKS & RAYS)

There are two family groups of fish: the elasmobranches, which are cartilaginous and include all the sharks and rays, and the teleosts, which are all other bony fishes. Sharks and rays are a highly specialized and ancient family present in every sea and ocean on the planet.

SHARKS

All sharks eat live food, but are also adept at scavenging decaying matter. Most are active hunters at night and all are shy. They are able to detect low-level electrical currents and can find sleeping fishes at night. Possessing highly developed sensory ampullae, they can detect low-frequency vibrations from great distances, as well as scent from injured or dying animals.

1 BASKING SHARK
Cetorhinus maximus
This is the largest shark inhabiting British waters, and the second largest fish in the world after the Whale Shark. It reaches lengths of up to 11m (37ft) and can weigh up to 7 tonnes. It is a harmless plankton feeder and is generally only seen in surface waters when it is feeding on swarms of plankton. Basking Sharks have enormous mouths and can filter 1,000–2,000 cubic metres of sea water every hour. Relatively little is known of their lives, other than that they travel up the west coast of the British Isles in large numbers and, as plankton and currents prevail, continue on into the North Sea.

2 LESSER-SPOTTED DOGFISH
Scyliorhinus caniculus
This fish is referred to as a 'dogfish', but it is actually in the cat shark family (Scyliorhinidae) and is perhaps the most common of the sharks in the North Sea and Baltic. Rarely over 1m (3ft 3in) long, its body is rough to the touch and covered in dark spots and blotches. It is commonly found in shallow water, and lays its eggs in May to September, usually on kelp stypes or even permanent moorings such as anchor chains. It attaches its 'mermaid's purse' egg case by four long, flexible tendrils.

3 NURSEHOUND
Scyliorhinus stellaris
The Nursehound grows to almost 2m (6ft 6in) in length. A purely nocturnal feeder, it preys on octopus, molluscs, crustaceans and demersal fishes. Due to its very sedentary nature, it has become a popular live catch for placement in marine aquaria.

4 SMOOTH HOUND
Mustelus mustelus
Growing to about 1.6m (5ft 4in) in length, this small, smooth-skinned shark has large eyes and a long, slender body with a sharply pointed snout and five gills. It has two large, almost equal-sized dorsal fins and an anal fin. Its main food is bony fishes, squid, octopus and small crustaceans. It is a bottom-dwelling species that stays in deep, dark water during the day, venturing into shallow water at night to hunt.

5 SPURDOG
Squalus acanthias
This shark has an obvious spur or spike that is directly attached and in front of the dorsal fin. The males reach over 1m (3ft 3in) in length. This is a slow-moving species that migrates from deeper waters into shallow estuaries to have its young during the summer months.

6 ANGEL SHARK
Squatina squatina
Growing to about 1.8m (6ft), this nocturnal bottom dweller is more like a large ray than a shark. Roughly diamond-shaped, it has large, fleshy pectoral fins, a rounded snout, a speckled body and a few small, fleshy appendages that dangle down on each side of its mouth. It stays buried in sand, lying in wait until a fish passes by its large mouth.

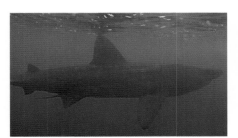

1 Basking Shark

2 Lesser-spotted Dogfish

3 Nursehound (*left*)
4 Smooth Hound (*above*)

5 Spurdog

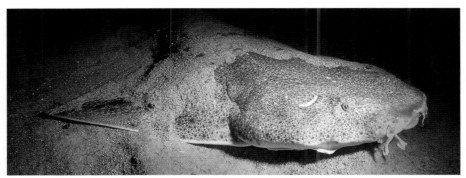

6 Angel Shark

RAYS

Rays are instantly recognizable by their pectoral fins, which are joined onto the head and form a broad skirt around the body. Although they have a cartilaginous skeleton like that of a shark, they do not have dorsal fins and their mouth parts are positioned on the underside of the body.

1 THORNBACK RAY
Raja clavata
This species grows to up to 90cm (3ft) in length, and has a roughly diamond-shaped body with a pattern of light spots over a uniform olive-green to light brown body colour. It is characterized by a series of short spines down its back and along its tail. A fairly common ray throughout the North Sea, it lives on fine sand or a gravel seabed, hunting for demersal fishes, molluscs and crustaceans. It is often caught in trawl nets as by catch.

2 COMMON SKATE
Raja batis
This ray has a long, elongated, pointed snout and is broadly kite-shaped. In adults, the back becomes partly prickly and 12–14 short spines develop along the tail. Common Skates are a rather drab olive-brown to grey colour on top and grey to creamy-white on the underside.

3 COMMON STINGRAY
Dasyatis pastinaca
Widely distributed but quite rare, the Common Stingray, which grows to 60cm (2ft) in length, is found from the Mediterranean all the way north to the Norwegian coastline. It prefers a sandy bottom where it can bury itself for protection during the day, and where it feeds on molluscs and small demersal fishes and crustaceans. It has one or two barbed spines at the base of its tail that can be whipped forwards and plunged into a predator in a purely defensive posture.

TELEOSTS OR BONY FISHES (ALL OTHER FISHES)

SALMON (FAMILY SALMONIDAE)

4 SALMON
Salmo salar
This large, robust fish can grow to 150cm (4ft 6in) in length and tends not to form schools, but rather small feeding groups that roam the North Sea and Atlantic. Salmon only start coming together in large groups when they approach the rivers of their birth to spawn. They feed on crustaceans and small fishes such as juvenile herring and cod, but neither the males nor the females feed while in fresh water. Wild salmon is only readily available in northern Scotland, Ireland and Norway – most of the salmon we eat is from farmed stock.

5 SEA TROUT
Salma trutta
The Sea Trout's tail is broader than that of salmon, and there are more obvious dark spots on its silvery, scaled flanks. It grows to over 120cm (4ft) in length. Like salmon, once mature it returns to its birth river to spawn. There are trout subspecies that live only in fresh water, such as the Brown Trout and Rainbow Trout.

CONGER EELS (CONGRIDAE)

6 CONGER EEL
Conger conger
The Conger Eel is greyish-blue in colour, cylindrical in shape and can grow to over 2m (6ft 7in) in length. It has a scaleless, snake-like body with a single dorsal fin, which merges into its tail and anal fins. The jaws are strong and it feeds on crustaceans and small fishes. Common throughout the entire North Sea region, it favours man-made habitats, particularly shipwrecks, where there is always an abundance of long, eel-shaped pipes for it to hide in.

1 Thornback Ray

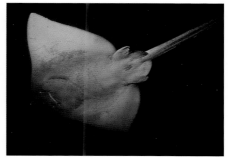

2 Common Skate (*above*)
3 Common Stingray (*left*)

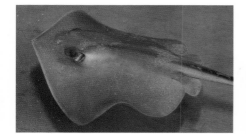

4 Salmon

5 Sea Trout

6 Conger Eel

PIPEFISHES
(FAMILY SYGNATHIDAE)

1 **GREAT PIPEFISH**
Sygnathus acus
Pipefishes are closely related to sea horses and, as the name implies, grow long and thin, with tube-like bodies that can be over 45cm (1ft 6in) long. The snout is more than half of the head length, and there is a distinct lump on the head behind the eyes. The body is ridged with obvious scaly plates. The dorsal fin is set near the rear of the body, and there are no anal or pectoral fins. Although the Great Pipefish is seen fairly regularly throughout the North Sea region and in some places can be extremely common, it is difficult to spot because it hides among swaying algae fronds.

2 **SNAKE PIPEFISH**
Entelurus aequorus
This is the largest pipefish species to be found in northern waters, and females may grow to as much as 60cm (23½in) in length. It is a uniform green to gold in colour, with transverse stripes down its flanks and a fairly oval appearance. In some areas it is extremely common in the summer months, and is preyed upon by seagulls. The Snake Pipefish is usually found among various algae, particularly the Sea Oak, *Halydris siliquosa*.

STICKLEBACKS
(FAMILY GASTEROSTEIDAE)

3 **THREE-SPINED STICKLEBACK**
Gasterosteus aculeatus
More commonly occurring in freshwater estuaries and rivers than in marine habitats, this stickleback can also be found around the shore. It can grow to 7.5cm (3in). While sticklebacks are usually a drab silvery-green and brown, during the mating season the male changes colour to bright red around the head and underside of the front of the body, emphasizing the blue-ringed eyes. During the spring, sticklebacks move to the sea and choose an area of protected pool that is only reached by extreme spring tides. Once the tides return to a normal flux, the sticklebacks are left behind and the pool gets diluted with rainwater and warms up. This creates a rich environment for the algae that the sticklebacks use to make the nests in which their eggs are laid. The eggs hatch in time for the following spring tide, and the young follow the brackish trail back into the river systems.

4 **FIFTEEN-SPINED STICKLEBACK**
Spinachia spinachia
Typically marine in nature, this stickleback grows to about 20cm (8in) in length and ranges from Norway into the Bay of Biscay. Usually found sub-tidally, it is rare in depths below 9m (30ft). Quite distinct in appearance, it has a long, slender snout. The dorsal and anal fins are situated directly before the start of the tail branch, and the dorsal fin has 14–17 spines. This species binds seaweeds together to form a nest from April to June, and the female deposits around 200 eggs in clusters encapsulated in a white membrane.

GURNARDS
(FAMILY TRIGLIDAE)

5 **TUB GURNARD**
Triglia lucerna
A large, robust fish with a stout, elongated head, the Tub Gurnard is principally red or pinkish-orange in colour and grows to up to 75cm (2ft 6in) in length. It has specially adapted pectoral fin rays that allow it to walk along the sandy sea floor. The young prefer muddy seabeds, and they have been observed diving into the substrate when danger threatens. Both juveniles and adults are found in small schools, and they are heard to emit small grunting noises. Tub Gurnards are frequently trapped as by catch in trawl nets.

1 Great Pipefish

2 Snake Pipefish

3 Three-spined Stickleback

4 Fifteen-spined Stickleback

5 Tub Gurnard

FLOUNDERS & FLATFISHES (FAMILIES SCOPTHALMIDAE & PLEURONECTIDAE)

1 TOPKNOT
Zeugopterus punctatus

The Topknot is more oval shaped than flat. Growing to 25cm (10in) long, it has a distinct fringe that is created by its dorsal and anal fins, which start just behind the head and continue to under the tail. It has a mottled coloration of brown, black and cream blotches with irregular dark spots, and uses this camouflage to great advantage, hiding under rocks and crevices. Ranging from Norway to the Bay of Biscay in depths down to 50m (165ft), this flatfish prefers rocky bottoms.

2 BLOCH'S TOPKNOT
Phrynorhombus regius

Very similar to the Topknot, *Zeugopterus punctatus*, Bloch's Topknot also prefers a rocky substrate, where it feeds on small crustaceans and fishes. It grows to only 20cm (8in) in length and is much more elongate and 'flounder-shaped' than the Topknot. Its body markings are similar, but Bloch's Topknot also has a more vivid pink and purple coloration in blotches around the head and upper body.

3 TURBOT
Scopthalmus maximus

A creature of deeper water, the Turbot is often encountered around shipwrecks. It can grow to over 1m (3ft 3in) in diameter, and is usually fairly circular in shape. The eyes are widely set and protruding, and the topside skin has no scales but is covered in rough, bony tubercles. This is a bottom-dwelling species that likes company and is quite often found in small groups. Spawning occurs in July and August: the four egg sacks are always carried in the left side of the body within a large cavity on both the top and bottom. Turbots can live to over 20 years of age. They are one of the largest flatfish species to be found in the North Sea, and their range extends from the Black Sea up to Iceland and beyond.

4 PLAICE
Pleuronectes platessa

A common fish, this flounder has very distinct red or orange spots on a uniformly light brown body top, while its undersides are pale cream or white in colour. Its eyes are raised and positioned alongside each other. It can grow to 1m (3ft 3in) in length, but is usually much smaller. This is an important commercially marketed species that is often found in estuaries and brackish water. It appears to be unafraid of divers.

5 DAB
Limanda limanda

Roughly diamond-shaped, this flounder can be recognized by the distinctive curved lateral line. Growing to approximately 33cm (15in) in length, it lives on soft bottoms, where it feeds on small fishes and invertebrates. Commonly found on the lower shore and caught by young would-be anglers in many coastal harbours throughout the region, the Dab spawns from January to August.

6 FLOUNDER
Platichthys flesus

The Flounder is multicoloured and usually flecked with light spots over a drab background. Its growth is very rapid and dependent on the abundance of food – adults can grow to as much as over 50cm (18in) in length. Triangular in shape, the dorsal and anal fins spread out into a fan shape towards the tail. Flounders live on fine sand or muddy bottoms and often enter brackish water in the search for mussels, small crabs and fishes.

1 Topknot (*above left*)
2 Bloch's Topknot (*above*)
3 Turbot (*inset left*)
4 Plaice (*below*)

5 Dab

6 Flounder

1 **WITCH**
Glyptocephalus cynoglossus
This species is similar in shape to the other flounders, but more oval. It can grow to over 50cm (18in) in length. Its eyes are placed very far forwards on the snout. The coloration is usually olive-green to brown, covered in light and dark spots. It is found in all regions of the North Sea.

ANGLERFISHES (FAMILY LOPHIIDAE)

2 **ANGLERFISH** or **MONK FISH**
Lophius piscatorius
This is an unmistakable-looking fish, not only because of its very wide head and fringed mantle, but also because it appears to be all mouth! Growing to over 2m (6ft 7in) long, the Anglerfish sits on the seabed and dangles a fleshy lure in front of its mouth. Once some hapless fish enters this danger zone, the fish rapidly opens its mouth and lunges upwards at the same time, sucking in huge quantities of water as well as the prey. Anglerfishes have a series of sharp, long-rayed spines that continue from behind the head to the tail. This is an important commercial species for the tail, which is firm flesh with no bones and is the part that is eaten.

3 **SHORT-SPINED ANGLERFISH**
Lophius budegassa
This fish is almost identical to the Anglerfish, *L. piscatorius*, apart from the fact that it has fewer rays on the dorsal fin and that the third ray is much shorter. It occurs in a similar habitat and its behaviour is similar. It is widely distributed throughout the North Sea and south to Senegal.

SCORPIONFISHES (FAMILY COTTIDAE)

Scorpionfishes are rather stout fishes that are bottom dwelling and have no swim-bladders for flotation. All are armed with venomous spines in their dorsal fins and have sharp spikes to their gill covers. They usually have warty protuberances, and can change their colour to suit their habitat and aid their excellent camouflage. They are opportunistic feeders and will decimate a home salt-water aquarium, eating everything in sight.

4 **BULL ROUT, FATHER-LASHER** or **SHORT-SPINED SEA SCORPION**
Myoxocephalus scorpius
This species usually grows to about 30cm (1ft) in length, but is generally much smaller. While it is a marine fish, it also appears to enjoy brackish water and can be found in river estuaries and harbours. It has a series of small spines along the body and a very wide, slightly flattened head. It lives on all substrate types, and is widely distributed throughout the range of the North Sea and south into the Bay of Biscay.

5 **LONG-SPINED SEA SCORPION**
Taurulus bubalis
This sea scorpion grows to only 15cm (6in) in length, and is usually much smaller. It is distinguished by its very obvious mouth barble or spine, as well as by a pair of significant spines behind the cheeks. It is multicoloured, and can change its coloration to suit its environment.

HOOKNOSES (FAMILY AGONIDAE)

6 **POGGE, HOOK-NOSE** or **ARMED BULLHEAD**
Agonus cataphractus
This is a curious little fish that can grow to up to 15cm (6in) in length, but rarely exceeds 10cm (4in). It has a generally mottled brown and cream appearance, a striking upturned or hooked nose and a number of fleshy barbels that hang below its chin. Feeding on small crabs and starfishes, it lives on all types of substrate and is quite often found in river estuaries, appearing to enjoy brackish waters.

1 Witch (*above*)
2 Anglerfish
(*above right*)

3 Short-spined
Anglerfish (*right*)
4 Bull Rout
(*below*)

5 Long-spined Sea Scorpion

6 Pogge

DRAGONETS
(FAMILY CALLIONYMIDAE)

1 DRAGONET
Callionymus lyra
The Dragonet is a bottom-dwelling fish with a flattened body and a roughly triangular-shaped head with a long lower jaw. The male grows to 30cm (1ft) in length, the female to 20cm (8in). The Dragonet's eyes are large, slightly protruding and set on top of the head. It has two dorsal fins, with the first fin on the male being long and triangular and the second rayed towards the tail. During the mating season, the males change colour: they have vivid blue markings around the jaw and eyes, and display their long, colourful dorsal fin.

SUCKERFISHES
(FAMILIES CYCLOPTERIDAE, LIPARIDIDAE & GOBIESOCIDAE)

2 LUMPSUCKER or SEA HEN
Cyclopterus lumpus
This species has a massive, stout body with a bony head and four rows of bony plates and tubercles. At 50cm (1ft 6in) in length, the females are usually twice the size of the males. During the breeding season the head area of the males changes to a brick-red or orange colour. The Lumpsucker is found on both sides of the Atlantic and south to Portugal. In the Baltic Sea it is harvested for its roe, which is sold as 'mock caviar' after being dyed some appropriate colour.

3 SEA SNAIL or
UNCTUOUS SUCKER
Liparis liparis
The body of this sea snail has a rounded front, and its dorsal and anal fins appear to join onto the tail. It has a sucker disc formed from the

modified pelvic fins, and is usually some drab colour that matches its environment, with a series of indistinct streaks and lines. It grows to 12cm (4.9in) in length but is usually much smaller, and feeds on small crustaceans.

4 MONTAGUE'S SEA SNAIL
Liparis montagui
This is a small, tadpole-shaped fish with a large and broad, rounded head, tapering top and thin tail. Similar to the Sea Snail, *L. liparis*, it has a single long dorsal fin, but this is not joined to its tail and is usually reddish-brown in colour. It can grow to as large as 10cm (4in) in length but is usually much smaller, and its pelvic fins have developed into a strong suction disc. The Montague's Sea Snail inhabits depths from the rocky shore to 30m (100ft), and hides among algae and small stones.

5 SHORE CLINGFISH
or CORNISH SUCKER
Lepadogaster lepadogaster
The Shore Clingfish has a body that is flattened sideways and a head that slopes gently into a long, duck-billed snout. The dorsal and anal fins are attached to the tail, and there are bluish spots or blotched markings behind the head. Variable in colour, it grows to about 7.5cm (3in) in length. It is found throughout the range of the North Sea and western Atlantic.

6 RUBY SUCKERFISH
Apletodon dentatus
Growing to about 5cm (2in) in length, this clingfish has a body that is flattened sideways and a head that is flattened from above. The suction disc is under the front part of the body, and the fish has enlarged cheeks, fairly large eyes and a wide mouth. It will change colour to suit its environment, but is most commonly reddish-brown. Feeding on small crustaceans and starfishes, the Ruby Suckerfish lives in all North Sea habitats.

1 Dragonet

2 Lumpsucker

3 Sea Snail

4 Montague's Sea Snail

5 Shore Clingfish

6 Ruby Suckerfish

COD & BASS TYPES (FAMILIES GADIDAE, MORONIDAE & SERRANIDAE)

1 POLLACK or LYTHE
Pollachius pollachius

Very similar to the Saithe, *P. virens*, this species is distinguished by its curved lateral line, which folds around its fins. It has three dorsal fins and relatively large eyes, and can grow to 50cm (3ft 3in) in length. The body is streamlined, with a forwards-jutting lower jaw. The Pollack is a commercially important species; it may be sold as Whiting, Whitefish or Haddock, depending on what the commercial market demands.

2 SAITHE, COALFISH or COLEY
Pollachius virens

Although this species is very similar to the Pollack, *P. pollachius*, the lateral line of the Saithe is straight and the jaws are of equal size. The Saithe is quite happy in brackish waters and is often caught by anglers at the mouths of local harbours all around the North Sea. It grows to a maximum length of 80cm (2ft 6 in), and like the Pollack, is a commercially important species.

3 COD
Gadus morhua

Once one of the principal commercially important fishes, this species has now reached threatened levels due to gross exploitation by ignorant governments and fishermen. Growing to 120cm (4ft) or more in length, it is an active hunter of young herring, Whiting and Haddock, and is always caught with these other species in trawl or seine nets. Generally spotted with brown over a grey, drab skin, it has a strong, light, curved lateral line, as well as a distinct fleshy barbel under the chin. This species prefers cooler temperatures of below 10°C, and extensive schools migrate to spawning and rearing grounds in various locations in both the North Sea and Baltic.

4 LING
Molva molva

Basically, this is a very long, thin cod (also with a fleshy barbel under the chin), which grows to almost 1.8m (6ft) in length. It can range from a rather drab, greyish-brown colour to having beautiful markings of fawn and cream along its flanks. The Ling is a solitary, shy fish that lives in caverns and crevices, but is quite often associated with Conger Eels, *Conger conger*, and squat lobsters. It feeds on other fishes, molluscs and crustaceans.

5 WHITING
Merlangius merlangius

The Whiting lives in small groups over sandy and muddy bottoms, where it feeds on small shrimps and fishes. During the juvenile stage, many young Whiting tend to gravitate into upper regions of the North Sea, where they form an association with large jellyfishes. This provides them with protection from predators – they are seemingly immune to the stinging cells of the jellyfishes. This is another commercially important species.

6 THREE-BEARDED ROCKLING
Gaidropsarus vulgaris

Usually reddish-brown in colour, this species has three obvious, fleshy appendages, two on the snout and a third under the chin. It grows to 50cm (1ft 8in) in length, and is a solitary fish. Preferring low light, it inhabits deeper caves, caverns and crevices, venturing out at night to feed. It is a very shy fish and will usually swim off when approached.

7 FIVE-BEARDED ROCKLING
Ciliata mustela

This species grows to up to 25cm (6in) in length, and is characterized by the five fleshy barbels on its snout – there is one each on either side of its nose cavities and three under the chin. Golden brown to dark brown in colour, it is quite a shy species that hides among stones and shell deposits. It is common in intertidal areas, and is distributed from Iceland to Portugal and the western Baltic Sea.

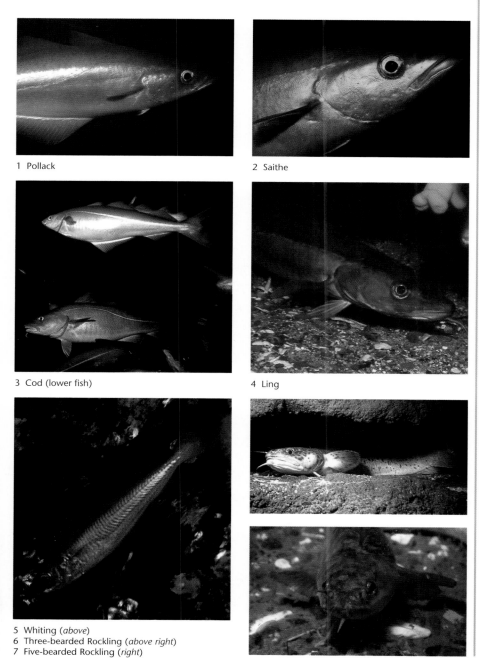

1 Pollack

2 Saithe

3 Cod (lower fish)

4 Ling

5 Whiting (*above*)
6 Three-bearded Rockling (*above right*)
7 Five-bearded Rockling (*right*)

1 SEA BASS
Dicentrarchus labrax
A silvery fish with strong, large scales, the Sea Bass can grow to around 1m (3ft 3in) in length and occurs in a number of different habitats. It is an active predator of other fishes, and is common in all coastal waters of the North Sea. Extremely popular in the commercial market, the Sea Bass is caught in the wild and also farm-reared.

2 COMBER
Serranus cabrilla
The Comber grows to about 30cm (1ft) in length, and is brownish in colour with darker vertical bands of brown, red or black. It has a well-defined jaw and is characterized by having a sawed edge on its anterior gill covers. It is quite a friendly species and is most commonly found in southern regions of the North Sea, south to the Mediterranean.

3 SAND EEL
Ammodytes tobianus
This is one of the most important fish species in the North Sea region. Many thousands of seabirds depend on it for their existence, and there is a very real danger that some fishermen are targeting the species for a quick profit, without thought for the future. It is a slender, eel-like fish with a protruding lower jaw, rarely exceeding 20cm (8in) in length. There are chevron-like markings on its belly scales and it has an indistinct lateral line. The Sand Eel is found in most sandy bays.

MACKEREL
(FAMILY SCOMBRIDAE)

4 MACKEREL
Scomber scombrus
This striking fish has a very streamlined body that is compressed laterally. Metallic in appearance, it has darker vertical and 'zigzag' bands down the body, and large eyes. The first dorsal fin is sail-like, and the anal and tail fins are deeply forked. Mackerel can grow to as much as 60cm (1ft 10in) in length. They hunt in small packs and are usually fished by the long-line method.

MULLET
(FAMILIES MULLIDAE
& MUGLIDAE)

5 RED MULLET
Mullus surmuletus
Most commonly seen in southern regions of the North Sea, the Red Mullet can be instantly recognized by its reddish-orange coloration and the two fleshy barbels under its chin. Sometimes known as the Goatfish, it uses its fleshy barbels in a sweeping motion to agitate soft substrates as an aid in its search for marine worms and molluscs. Red Mullet usually work in small groups, and are quite approachable.

6 GREY or BOXLIP MULLET
Oedalechilus labeo
Grey Mullet are a uniform silver-grey in colour with thin, brownish lines along the flanks, and grow to about 25cm (10in) in length. They have large, fleshy lips with which they 'hoover' fine silt layers from rocky surfaces, but are most commonly seen feeding at the surface on plankton debris and algae scum. A schooling species, they are seen in most habitats, but generally in southern regions of the North Sea; however, their range is continuing further north and they are now found in northern Europe and Scotland.

WEAVERFISHES
(FAMILY TRACHINIDAE)

7 GREAT WEAVER
Trachinus draco
Weaverfishes are long and thin, and hide almost completely under the sand, waiting for prey to come anywhere near their heavily armed, upturned mouths. They grow to about 40cm (1ft 4in) long, and have wide, hinged mouths. The flanks are tan to lightish-blue in colour, and the back of the head is mottled. The first dorsal fin has three adapted spines, used for defence. The spines are venomous, with poison glands at their bases. In southern areas of the North Sea, Great Weavers can be a problem in tidal flats – they favour very shallow water and people playing on the beach have been known to stand on them accidentally.

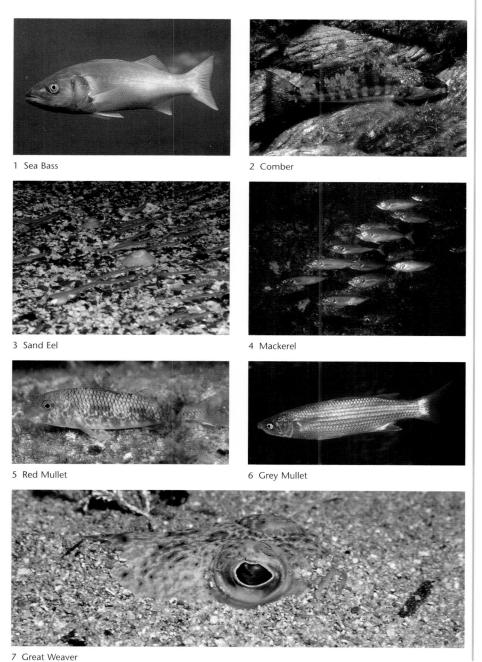

1 Sea Bass

2 Comber

3 Sand Eel

4 Mackerel

5 Red Mullet

6 Grey Mullet

7 Great Weaver

WRASSES
(FAMILY LABRIDAE)

Wrasses comprise a large and diverse family that occurs throughout the Atlantic, North Sea, Baltic and Mediterranean. Most of the species are carnivorous, living on small crustaceans and molluscs, and a few have very strong jaws with which to crush sea urchins. Wrasses are found around all coastlines of the North Sea, quite often in large numbers, and one of the most common species is the Ballan Wrasse, *Labrus bergylta*.

All members of this family share common characteristics, namely body length around three times the height; large, fleshy, protruding lips and prominent eyes, set high on the head; one low dorsal fin and short, rounded pectoral fins. A number of the juveniles of certain species act as cleaners to other fishes, and most go through various colour changes as they reach maturity.

1 **BALLAN WRASSE**
Labrus bergylta
The most common of the wrasse species in the North Sea, this species has a mottled brown skin with clearly defined scales. It can grow to 45cm (1ft 6in) in length, and has a high, convex head with steeply sloping brow and large, fleshy lips. There is an intricate network pattern around its head and lower jaw. An inquisitive fish, the Ballan Wrasse is easy to approach and will follow divers around in case they stir up anything worth eating.

2 **CORKWING WRASSE**
Symphodus melops
This species has a darker blotch across the forehead and a varied coloration, with vertical bands of golden-brown and cream. Growing to approximately 30cm (1ft) in length, it has a high dorsal fin, dark bands at the tail and blue radiating stripes at the head and lower jaw. The Corkwing Wrasse is relatively common in southern waters of the North Sea, and prefers to live close to shore among kelp and boulders.

3 **CUCKOO WRASSE**
Labrus bimaculatus
One of the most colourful of the wrasse family, the Cuckoo Wrasse can grow to as much as 35cm (1ft 2in) in length. During the mating season, the male changes from a rich, golden-brown colour to having brilliant blue markings and stripes around the front of the head and flanks, then changing to its usual golden-brown colour, before once more becoming blue at the tail. The female is golden-brown with three dark markings surrounded by white, which are found at the base of the dorsal fin. This species prefers coastal areas, rocky reefs and shipwrecks that contain many nooks and crannies in which it can hide. The Cuckoo Wrasse is relatively common in the extreme south and extreme north of the North Sea, with rarely any presence in the south of Scotland or north-east England.

4 **GOLDSINNY**
Ctenolabrus rupestris
A small species of wrasse growing to 15cm (6in) in length, the Goldsinny is light brown to golden-brown in colour and has a distinctive black blotch on the top of and start of the tail. Prominent buck teeth and widely set, protruding eyes are also characteristic of this species. The Goldsinny is widely distributed among most algae and lives close to the shore, where it hunts in small groups.

5 **ROCK COOK**
Centrolabrus exoletus
This small species resembles the Corkwing Wrasse, *Symphodus melops*, but is distinguished by the lack of the dark blotch behind the eye and dark bands at the tail root. The male has pretty blue display lines under the eye and blue-spotted markings towards the rear of the body, fins and tail during the mating season. The Rock Cook grows to only about 12cm (4¾in) in length. It is most commonly found in southern areas of the North Sea, although it has also been recorded in south-east Scotland as well as in southern parts of Scandinavia.

1 Ballan Wrasse

2 Corkwing Wrasse

3 Cuckoo Wrasse (male, *right*, and female, *left*)

4 Goldsinny

5 Rock Cook

GOBIES
(FAMILY GOBIIDAE)

Gobies have two dorsal fins and hold themselves quite rigidly when at rest. The pelvic fins are generally modified into a sucker disc, which keeps the fish securely in place while balanced precariously on an underhanging rock ledge.

1 BLACK GOBY
Gobius niger
This is a large goby that grows to 15cm (6in) in length. Sexually mature at two years of age, the territorial males and juveniles are black (hence the name) and have a life span of around five years. The Black Goby inhabits harbours and brackish waters, in estuaries, coastal lagoons and sea lochs. Its distribution covers northern Norway into the Baltic, North Sea, Mediterranean, Black Sea and Canary Islands.

2 FRIE'S GOBY
Leseurigobius friesi
Found in association with the Scampi Prawn, *Nephrops norvegicus*, the Frie's Goby appears to have a symbiotic relationship with this large prawn. However, little is known of its habits other than that it will hide in the prawn's burrows and is found wherever there are Scampi Prawns. It is pale mottled mauve and cream in colour, with golden-yellow spots over its flanks. It is known to breed from May to August and grows to 10cm (4in) in length.

3 SAND GOBY
Pomatoschistus minutus
This is a common bottom-dwelling goby that grows to 4.5cm (3in) in length. Its sandy, mottled brown and sandy speck coloration helps to keep it camouflaged, and it usually occurs in relatively shallow waters less than 18m (60ft) deep. It is often found in small groups.

4 LEOPARD-SPOTTED GOBY
Thorogobius ephippiatus
Another very distinctive goby that cannot be confused with any other species, the Leopard-spotted Goby grows to 13cm (5in) in length and is covered in dark purplish blotches on a pink-blue background. Often found in

association with the Strident Squat Lobster, *Galathea strigosa*, it prefers low light and is an active predator at night, feeding on small crustaceans and worms. Widely distributed throughout the North Sea as well as the Mediterranean and Black Seas, it is quite a sociable fish that often lives in small groups at the entrances to small, rocky crevices or caverns that abut onto a soft, sandy seabed.

5 TWO-SPOT GOBY
Gobiusculus flavescens
This is a small, slender goby that is usually seen in the cooler winter months, living among hydroids, bryozoans and various algae. Its background colour is reddish-brown with dark markings and pale saddles. It grows to up to about 5cm (2in) in length, and is usually seen in small hunting groups. The male has a dark spot on its sides, near the first dorsal fin, and both sexes have a dark spot at the base of the tail fin.

BLENNIES
(FAMILY BLENNIIDAE)

This is a large family of small fishes that live around coastal waters and share common characteristics. They favour rocky crevices and tend to perch near their entrances. Most blennies have fleshy appendages above their high-set eyes and, although they resemble gobies, they generally have shorter, blunt heads, prominent lips, pectoral fins that are more like feet, and a single or triple dorsal fin. They lie in a flexed position and are usually easy to approach.

6 TOMPOT BLENNY
Parablennius gattorugine
One of the largest and gaudiest of the blennies, the Tompot Blenny has a thickset body tapering to a slender tail. Its forehead is high and convex, and it has two very conspicuous, branched appendages above the eyes, resembling fleshy antlers. It grows to 25cm (10in) in length, and has seven wide, dark brown, vertical bands on the body, which is varicoloured from brown to tan and red. This is a wide-ranging species that can be seen inhabiting holes with only its head protruding.

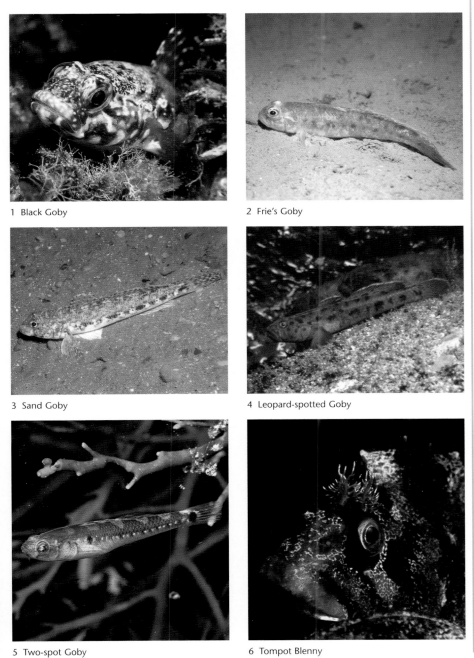

1 Black Goby

2 Frie's Goby

3 Sand Goby

4 Leopard-spotted Goby

5 Two-spot Goby

6 Tompot Blenny

1 SHANNY
Lipophrys pholis

This is quite a large, aggressive fish with a large head and wide, fleshy lips. Similar to the Tompot Blenny, *Parablennius gattorugine*, it is usually mottled green and cream in colour, but it has no fleshy appendages above its eyes, which are set high on its head. It is common intertidally and is often seen in rockpools, where it lays its eggs under stones and algae; during the summer months, many coastal rockpools are filled with juveniles. The Shanny is found all around the British Isles, northern Europe and southern Norway.

2 YARRELL'S BLENNY
Chirolophis ascani

This is a long, slender blenny with a single, unnotched dorsal fin that runs all the way to its tail. Growing to up to 25cm (10in) in length, it has brown, beige and cream mottled markings all over its body, and its narrow head has two large, tufted protuberances above the eyes and at the start of the dorsal fin. There is a dark ring around each eye and dark vertical bands on the body. Although this fish resembles the true blennies, it is actually a member of another family group, the Arctic blennies (Stichaeidae). Once thought to be quite rare, it is in fact relatively common in northern areas.

3 BUTTERFISH or GUNNEL
Pholis gunnellus

This is an eel-like fish growing to about 25cm (10in) in length. It has a single, sharply edged dorsal fin that runs the entire length of its body. It is variable in colour from brown through tan, but its most obvious characteristic is the rows of 12 or more light-ringed dark spots along each flank at the base of the dorsal fin. Although the Butterfish is found throughout the region and generally prefers shallow water, it has been observed in most habitats, including deep ship-wrecks and areas with strong currents.

WOLF FISHES
(FAMILY ANARHICHADIDAE)

4 WOLF FISH or CATFISH
Anarhichas lupus

The largest of the goby-shaped fishes, the Wolf Fish is ferocious looking due to its large, prominent set of teeth, which protrude out from its wide, fleshy jaw and a face that only a mother could love! Growing to around 1m (3ft 3in) in length, it has a long, slender body with a single dorsal fin that starts just behind the head and continues to the tail, and an anal fin that starts midway down the underside of the body and also reaches the tail. The skin is tough and leathery looking, and bluish-grey in colour. The male and female of this species are often found together in the same holes. Their strong jaws and teeth are ideal for crushing sea urchins and eating crabs. This is a northern and Arctic species that is rarely found below southern Scotland.

SUNFISHES
(FAMILY MOLIDAE)

5 SUNFISH
Mola mola

A curious visitor to the North Sea zone, this fish is an Atlantic or Mediterranean wanderer. It has a disc-shaped body, leathery skin and no scales. The tail is no more than a leathery frill, but it has a large dorsal fin and anal fin that it uses to great effect for propulsion. It has a small mouth and a blunt snout, large, prominent eyes and small pectoral fins. Usually greyish-blue in colour, the Sunfish is an infrequent visitor to the North Sea region, most likely to be seen near the surface.

1 Shanny

2 Yarrell's Blenny

3 Butterfish

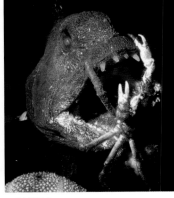

4 Wolf Fish

5 Sunfish

TURTLES

1 LEATHERBACK TURTLE
Dermochelys coriacea
There are no records of breeding turtles within the North Sea region, but the strong tidal streams from the North Atlantic drift can bring curious and rare visitors to the coastline. The photographs opposite of a netted Leatherback Turtle are from St Abbs Head in south-east Scotland. It was rescued from nets, loaded on board a lorry and successfully reintroduced into the sea on the west coast of Scotland.

MAMMALS

The mammal populations in and around the North Sea include dolphins, porpoises and other cetaceans, as well as otters and seals.

CETACEANS

There are different cetaceans living within and outside the North Sea zone, including several whales, dolphins and porpoises. While more attention is now being focused on these wonderful creatures and their economic benefit through sightseeing visitors, they are all considered endangered due to the high levels of pollution encountered in some areas, as well as the danger from being caught accidentally in fishing nets and lines.

2 BOTTLENOSE DOLPHIN
Tursiops truncatus
The Bottlenose Dolphin is the most commonly encountered dolphin within the North Sea area and there are several areas that contain resident populations, including the Moray Firth in the north-east of Scotland. The mammal has an attractive, friendly-looking face with a long snout and high forehead, and grows to as much as 4m (13ft) in length. The Bottlenose Dolphin enjoys riding the bow waves of fast boats and is usually encountered in family groups.

3 ORCA or KILLER WHALE
Orcinus orca
Orcas are members of the oceanic dolphin family and are found in all of the world's oceans. They are occasionally seen in most parts of the North Sea, but particularly in the northern Norwegian fjords, where they come to hunt the migrating shoals of herring. Orcas are versatile and opportunistic predators that mainly hunt fishes, but will also attack juvenile whales and other dolphins. They are highly social animals, and are regarded as an endangered species. Wild Orcas are not considered to be a threat to divers.

SEALS

Two species of seal are found around the shores of the North Sea: the Grey Seal and the Common Seal. An estimated 85,000 Grey Seals – well over half the world's population – and about 25,000 Common Seals live around Britain. There is a huge breeding colony of over 6,000 seals in the Wash, and many other colonies up and down the coastline.

4 GREY SEAL
Halichoerus grypus
The Grey Seal has a nominal length of about 2m (6ft 7in), with males weighing up to 350kg (770lb) and females up to 250kg (550lb). The colour of the coat varies from grey to brown and silver, and is usually mottled with varying colour blotches. The males (bulls) can usually be distinguished from the females by the pattern of colours in their fur. In the males, the predominant background colour is dark, but in the females it is light. Juveniles are born with a creamy-white natal coat. In Europe, most Grey Seals are found around the British Isles, but there is also a large, endangered colony in the Baltic Sea.

1 Leatherback Turtle

2 Bottlenose Dolphin

3 Orca

4 Grey Seal

INDEX

Photographs are indicated
by **bold** page numbers.

Abietinaria abietina 38, **39**
Acanthochitona crinitus 76,
  77
Acanthodoris pilosa 90, **91**
Acmaea virginea 76, **77**
Actinia equina 44, **45**
Adalaria proxima 90, **91**
Adamsia carciniopados 46,
  47
Adocia cineria 34, **35**
Aeolidia papillosa 88, **89**
Aequipecten opercularis 82,
  83
Aglophenia pluma 40, **41**
Agonus cataphractus 110,
  111
Alaria esculenta 26, **27**
Alcyonidium diaphanum 52,
  53
Alcyonium digitatum 50
Alentia gelatinosa 54, **55**
Algae Squat Lobster 64, **65**
Ammodytes tobianus 116,
  117
Amphilectus fucorum 34, **35**
Anarhichas lupus 122, **123**
Ancula gibbosa 88, **89**
Anemone Sea Spider 72, **73**
Anemonia viridis 44, **45**
Angel Shark 102, **103**
Anglerfish 110, **111**
Antedon bifida 92, **93**
Antedon petasus 92, **93**
Aphrodite aculeate 54, **55**
Apletodon dentatus 112,
  113
Aplidium punctum 98, **99**
Aplysia punctata 84, **85**
Apolemia uvaria 42, **43**
Aporrhais pespelicani 80, **81**
Aqueorea aequorea 42, **43**
Archidoris pseudoargus 90,
  91
Arctic Cowie 80, **81**
Arctic Ice Shrimp 62, **63**
Arenicola marina 54, **55**
Armed Bullhead 110, **111**
Ascidia mentula 98, **99**
Ascophyllum nodosum 27,
  28
Aslia lefevrei 96, **97**
Astacilla longicornis 70
Asterias rubens 94, **95**
Astropecten irregularis 92, **93**
Atelecyclus rotundatus 68,
  69
Aurelia aurita 42, **43**
Axinella infundibuliformis 34,
  35

Baked-bean Ascidian 100,
  101
Balanus balanus 60, **61**
Balanus crenatus 60, **61**
Ballan Wrasse 118, **119**
Baltic Isopod 70, **71**

Banded Chink Shell 78, **79**
Banded Cingulla 78, **79**
Basking Shark 102, **103**
Beadlet Anemone 44, **45**
Bell Hydroid 36, **37**
Bell Jellyfish 42, **43**
Bertella plumula 84, **85**
Berthella 84, **85**
Black Brittlestar 92, **93**
Black Goby 120, **121**
Bladder-Locks 26
Bladder Wrack 28, **29**
Bloch's Topknot 108, **109**
Bloody Henry 94, **95**
Blue-leg Swimming Crab
  68, **69**
Blue-rayed Limpet 76, **77**
Bolinopsis 42, **43**
Bolinopsis infundibulum 42,
  43
Bolocera tuediae 48, **49**
Bootlace Weed 22, **23**
Bootlace Worm 54, **55**
Botrylloides leachii 100, **101**
Botryllus schlosseri 100, **101**
Bottlebrush Hydroid 38, **39**
Bottlenose Dolphin 124,
  125
Boxup Mullet 116, **117**
Branching Sea Beard 38, **39**
Bristle Worm 54, **55**
Broad-clawed Porcelain Crab
  68, **69**
Brown Chiton 76, **77**
Brown Doris 90, **91**
Brown Mane 24, **25**
Brown Shrimp 60, **61**
Buccinum undatum 80, **81**
Buckie 80, **81**
Bugula 52, **53**
Bugula turbinata 52, **53**
Bull Rout 110, **111**
Burrowing Anemone 44, **45**
Burrowing Sea Cucumber
  96, **97**
Burrowing Starfish 92, **93**
Butterfish 122, **123**

Calamari 74, **75**
Caligus elongatus 72, **73**
Callionymus lyra 112, **113**
Calliostoma zizyphinum 78,
  79
Cancer pagurus 68, **69**
Caprella linearis 72, **73**
Carcinus maenus 70, **71**
Carpet Coral 48, **49**
Caryophyllia smithii 48, **49**
Catfish 122, **123**
Centrolabrus exoletus 118,
  119
Cerastoderma edule 82, **83**
Cerianthus lloydii 44, **45**
Cetorhinus maximus 102,
  103
Chaetogammarus marinus
  72, **73**
Chimney Polymastia 34, **35**
Chirolophis ascani 122, **123**

Chorda filum 22
Ciliata mustela 114, **115**
Cingula cingillus 78, **79**
Ciona intestinalis 98, **99**
Circular Crab 68, **69**
Clathrina coriacea 32, **33**
Clathrina Sponge 32, **33**
Clavelina lepadiformis 98, **99**
Cloak Anemone 46, **47**
Cluster Sea Squirt 100, **101**
Coarse Feather Hydroid 38,
  39
Cockle 82, **83**
Cod 114, **115**
Codium bursa 22, **23**
Coley 114, **115**
Colonial Sea Squirt 100,
  101
Comber 116, **117**
Common Barnacle 60, **61**
Common Cuttlefish 74, **75**
Common Grey Sea Slug 88,
  89
Common Heart Urchin 96,
  97
Common Hermit Crab 64,
  65
Common Limpet 76, **77**
Common Lobster 62, **63**
Common Mussel 84, **85**
Common Periwinkle 78, **79**
Common Sea Squirt 98, **99**
Common Sea Urchin 94, **95**
Common Shore Crab 70,
  71
Common Skate 104, **105**
Common Squid 74, **75**
Common Starfish 94, **95**
Common Stingray 104,
  105
Common Sunstar 94, **95**
Communal Cup Coral 48,
  49
Conger conger 104, **105**
Conger Eel 104, **105**
Corallina 30, **31**
Corallina officinalis 30, **31**
Corella 18, 100, **101**
Corella parallelogramma
  100, **101**
Corkwing Wrasse 118, **119**
Coronet Nudibranch 88, **89**
Corynactis viridis 46, **47**
Coryphella lineata 88, **89**
Corystes cassivelaunus 68,
  69
Crangon crangon 60, **61**
Crossaster papposus 94, **95**
Crossed Jellyfish 42, **43**
Crystal Tips 88, **89**
Ctenolabrus rupestris 118,
  119
Cuckoo Wrasse 118, **119**
Curled Octopus 74, **75**
Cuthona concinna 90, **91**
Cyanea capillata 40, **41**
Cyclopterus lumpus 112, **113**

Dab 108, **109**

Dahlia Anemone 46, **47**
Dasyatis pastinaca 104, **105**
Dead-Man's Fingers 50, **51**
Deepwater Dahlia 44, **45**
Delesseria sanguinea 30, **31**
Delicate Coral Worm 56, **57**
Dendrodoa grossularia 100,
  101
Dendronotus frondosus 86,
  87
Dermochelys coriacea 124
Designer Spider Crab 66,
  67
Devil Crab 70, **71**
Devonshire Cup Coral 48,
  49
Diazone violacea 98, **99**
Dicentrarchus labrax 116,
  117
Dictyosiphon spp. 24, **25**
Dictyota dichotoma 24, **25**
Didemnum albidum 100,
  101
Dinophysis norvegica 13
Dog Whelk 80, **81**
Doto coronata 90, **91**
Doto pinnatifida 90, **91**
Dragonet 112, **113**

Echinocardium cordatum 96,
  97
Echinus esculentus 94, **95**
Edible Crab 68, **69**
Edible Whelk 80, **81**
Edible Winkle 78, **79**
Eelgrass 22, **23**
Eelgrass Anemone 48, **49**
Electra pilosa 52, **53**
Eledone cirrhosa 74, **75**
Elegant Anemone 46, **47**
Elegant Shrimp 60, **61**
Encrusting Alga 30, **31**
Encrusting Sponge 34, **35**
Ensis siliqua 82, **83**
Entelurus aequorus 106, **107**
Enteromorpha intestinalis 22,
  23
Epizoanthus couchii 44, **45**
Erect Bryozoan 52, **53**
Eualus gaimardii 62, **63**
Eubranchus farrani 90, **91**
Eunicella verrucosa 50, **51**
Eupolymnia nebulosa 58, **59**
European Cowie 80, **81**
European Lobster 62, **63**
Euspira catena 80, **81**

Facelina bostoniensis 88, **89**
Facelina coronata 88, **89**
Father-Lasher 110, **111**
Feather Starfish 92, **93**
Fiddler Crab 70, **71**
Fifteen-spined Stickleback
  106, **107**
Filograna implexa 56, **57**
Finger Bryozoan 52, **53**
Five-bearded Rockling 114,
  115
Flabellina pedata 88, **89**

Flame Shell 82, **83**
Flat Periwinkle 78, **79**
Flounder 108, **109**
Flustra foliacea 52, **53**
Football-Jersey Worm 54, **55**
Football Sea Squirt 98, **99**
Four-lined Nudibranch 52, **53**, 86, **87**
Fragile Brittlestar 92, **93**
Frie's Goby 120, **121**
Frond Nudibranch 86, **87**
Fucus ceranoides **27**, 28
Fucus serratus 28, **29**
Fucus spiralis 28, **29**
Fucus vesiculosus sus 28, **29**
Funiculina quadrangularis 50, **51**
Furbellows 26, **27**
Fuzzy Doris 90, **91**

Gadus morhua 114, **115**
Gaidropsarus vulgaris 114, **115**
Galathea dispersa 64, **65**
Galathea nexa 64, **65**
Galathea strigosa 64, **65**
Gasterosteus aculeatus 106, **107**
Ghost Shrimp 72, **73**
Gibbula cineraria 78, **79**
Glyptocephalus cynoglossus 110, **111**
Gobius niger 120, **121**
Gobiusculus flavescens 120, **121**
Goldsinny 118, **119**
Goniodoris nodosa 86, **87**
Gorgonocephalus caputmedusae 92, **93**
Great Pipefish 106, **107**
Great Scallop 82, **83**
Great Spider Crab 66, **67**
Great Weaver 116, **117**
Green Isopod 70, **71**
Grey Mullet 116, **117**
Grey Seal **17**, 124, **125**
Grey Topshell 78, **79**
Gunnel 122, **123**
Gymnangium montagui 40, **41**

Hairy-clawed Lobster 64, **65**
Hairy Kelp 26, **27**
Hairy Sea Mat 52, **53**
Halecium halecium 38, **39**
Halichoerus grypus 124, **125**
Halichondria bowerbanki 34, **35**
Halydris siliquosa 24, **25**
Harbour Crab 68, **69**
Harlequin Shrimp 60, **61**
Harmathoë impar 54, **55**
Hediste diversicolor 56, **57**
Helcion pellucidum 76, **77**
Henricia sanguinolenta 94, **95**
Hermit Crab Hydroid 38, **39**
Hermit Crab Sponge 32
Herringbone Hydroid 38, **39**

Himanthalia elongate 24, **25**
Hippolyte inermis 62, **63**
Hippolyte longirostris 62, **63**
Hippolyte varians 60, **61**
Homarus gammarus 62, **63**
Hook-Nose 110, **111**
Hoplangia durotrix 48, **49**
Horned Strap Wrack 52, **53**
Horned Wrack **27**, 28
Hornwrack 52, **53**
Horse Mussel 84, **85**
100-legged Crinoid 92, **93**
Hyas araneus 66, **67**
Hyas coarctatus 66, **67**
Hydractinia echinata 38, **39**
Hydrallmania falcata 38, **39**

Idotea baltica 70, **71**
Idotea granulosa 70, **71**
Inachus dorsettensis 66, **67**
Inachus phalangium 66, **67**
Ink Fish 74, **75**
Inquisitive Tube Worm 58, **59**

Jania 30, **31**
Jania rubens 30, **31**
Janolus cristatus 88, **89**
Jassa 70, **71**
Jassa falcata 70, **71**
Jewel Anemone 46, **47**

Killer Whale 124, **125**
Knotted Wrack **27**, 28

Labrus bergylta 118, **119**
Labrus bimaculatus 118, **119**
Lacuna vincta 78, **79**
Laminaria digitata 24, **25**
Laminaria hyperborea 26, **27**, 30
Laminaria polyschides 26, **27**
Laminaria saccharina 26, **27**
Langoustine 62, **63**
Lanice conchilega 58, **59**
Leatherback Turtle 124
Leopard-spotted Goby 120, **121**
Lepadogaster lepadogaster 112, **113**
Leptomysis gracilis 72, **73**
Leseurigobius friesi 120, **121**
Lesser Octopus 74, **75**
Lesser-spotted Dogfish 102, **103**
Light-bulb Tunicate 98, **99**
Limacea clavigera 86, **87**
Limanda limanda 108, **109**
Limaria hians 82, **83**
Lined Tritonia 86, **87**
Lineus longissimus 54, **55**
Ling 114, **115**
Liocarcinus depurator 68, **69**
Liocarcinus navigator 68, **69**
Lion's Mane Jellyfish 40, **41**
Liparis liparis 112, **113**
Liparis montagui 112, **113**
Lipophrys pholis 122, **123**
Lithophyllum incrustans 30, **31**
Little Cuttlefish 74, **75**

Littorina littorea 78, **79**
Littorina obtusata 78, **79**
Loligo forbesii 74, **75**
Long-armed Spider Crab 66, **67**
Long-clawed Squat Lobster 64, **65**
Long-spine Shrimp 62, **63**
Long-spined Sea Scorpion 110, **111**
Lophius budegassa 110, **111**
Lophius piscatorius 110, **111**
Lug Worm 54, **55**
Luidia ciliaris 94, **95**
Lumpsucker 112, **113**
Lyre Crab 66, **67**
Lythe 114, **115**

Mackerel 116, **117**
Macropodia tenuirostris 66, **67**
Maerle 30, **31**
Marthasterias glacialis 94, **95**
Masked Crab 68, **69**
Medusa Basket Star 92, **93**
Membranipora membranacea 52, **53**
Membranoptera 30, **31**
Membranoptera alata 30, **31**
Merlangius merlangius 114, **115**
Metridium senile 46, **47**
Modiolus modiolus 84, **85**
Mola mola 122, **123**
Molva molva 114, **115**
Monkfish 110, **111**
Montague's Sea Snail 112, **113**
Moon Jellyfish 42, **43**
Morcellium argus 100, **101**
Mud Worm 58, **59**
Muddy Brittlestar 92, **93**
Mullus surmuletus 116, **117**
Multicoloured Chiton 76, **77**
Munida rugosa 64, **65**
Mussel Hydroid 38, **39**
Mustelus mustelus 102, **103**
Mya arenaria 82, **83**
Myoxocephalus scorpius 110, **111**
Mytilus edulis 84, **85**
Myxicola infundibulum 58, **59**
Myxilla incrustans 34, **35**

Nassarius reticulatus 78, **79**
Necklace Shell 80, **81**
Necora puber 70, **71**
Nemertesia antennina 38, **39**
Nemertesia ramosa 38, **39**
Neopendactyla mixta 96, **97**
Nephrops norvegicus 62, **63**
Netted Dog Whelk 78, **79**
Node Doris 86, **87**
Northern Henricia 94, **95**
Northern Polycera 86, **87**
Northern Sea Fan 50, **51**
Northern Sea Urchin 96, **97**

Norway Lobster 62, **63**
Nucella lapillus 80, **81**
Nursehound 102, **103**
Nymphon gracile 72, **73**

Obelia 36, **37**
Obelia geniculata 36, **37**
Oedalechilus labeo 116, **117**
Onchidoris fusca 90, **91**
Onchidoris luteocincta 86, **87**
Ophiocomino nigra 92, **93**
Ophiothrix fragilis 92, **93**
Ophiura albida 92, **93**
Opposum Shrimp 72, **73**
Orange Mat Sponge 34, **35**
Orcinus orca 124, **125**

Pagarus bernhardus 64, **65**
Pagarus prideaux 64, **65**
Painted Topshell 78, **79**
Palaemon elegans 60, **61**
Palaemon montagui 60, **61**
Pale Bristle Worm 54, **55**
Parablennius gattorugine 120, **121**
Parasitic Gadoid Louse 72, **73**
Patella vulgata 76, **77**
Pawsonia saxicola 96, **97**
Peachia 46, **47**
Peachia cylindrica 46, **47**
Peacock Worm 56, **57**
Pecten maximus 82, **83**
Pelican's-foot Shell 80, **81**
Penneatula phosphorea 50, **51**
Peppermint Shrimp 62, **63**
Pholis gunnellus 122, **123**
Phosphorescent Sea Pen 50, **51**
Phrynorhombus regius 108, **109**
Phymatolithon calcareum 30, **31**
Pink Anemone 48, **49**
Pink Sea Squirt 98, **99**
Pink Shrimp 60, **61**
Plaice 108, **109**
Platichthys flesus 108, **109**
Pleurobrachia pileus 42, **43**
Pleuronectes platessa 108, **109**
Plumed Hydroid 40, **41**
Plumose Anemone 46, **47**
Pod Razor 82, **83**
Pododesmus patelliformis 84, **85**
Pogge 110, **111**
Pollachius pollachius 114, **115**
Pollachius virens 114, **115**
Pollack 114, **115**
Polycera faeroensis 86, **87**
Polycera quadrilineata 52, **53**, 86, **87**
Polymastia 34, **35**
Polymastia boletiformis 34, **35**
Polymastia mamillaris 34, **35**
Pomatocerous triqueter 56, **57**

Pomatoschistus minutus 120, **121**
Porania pulvillus 94, **95**
Porcellana platycheles 68, **69**
Porella compressa 52, **53**
Prideaux's Hermit Crab 64, **65**
Protanthea simplex 48, **49**
Psammechinus miliaris 96, **97**
Pseudosuberites sulphereus 32, **33**
Psolus phantapus 96, **97**
Purple Heart Urchin 96, **97**
Purple Nudibranch 88, **89**
Purse Sponge 32, **33**
Pycogonum littorale 72, **73**

Queen Scallop 82, **83**
Queenie 82, **83**

Rag Worm 56, **57**
Raja batis 104, **105**
Raja clavata 104, **105**
Raspalia ramose 34, **35**
Red Burrowing Sea Cucumber 96, **97**
Red Chiton 76, **77**
Red Cushion Star 94, **95**
Red Mullet 116, **117**
Red Sunstar 94, **95**
Red Tube Worm 58, **59**
Rhizostoma octopus 42, **43**
Rib Weed 26, **27**
Ribbed Saddle Oyster 84, **85**
Rock Cook 118, **119**
Ruby Suckerfish 112, **113**

Sabella pavonina 56, **57**
Sagartia elegans 46, **47**
Sagartiogeton laceratus 48, **49**
Sagartiogeton viduatus 48, **49**
Saithe **6**, 114, **115**
Salma trutta 104, **105**
Salmacina Coral Worm 56, **57**
Salmacina dysteri 56, **57**
Salmo salar 104, **105**
Salmon 104, **105**
Sand Crab 68, **69**
Sand Eel 116, **117**
Sand Gaper 82, **83**

Sand Goby 120, **121**
Sand-Hopper 72, **73**
Sand Mason 58, **59**
Sandy Creeplet 44, **45**
Scallop Sponge 32, **33**
Scampi 62, **63**
Scomber scombrus 116, **117**
Scopthalmus maximus 108, **109**
Scorpian Spider Crab 66, **67**
Scottish Coral 30
Scyliorhinus caniculus 102, **103**
Scyliorhinus stellaris 102, **103**
Scypha compressa 32, **33**
Sea Bass 116, **117**
Sea Beard 38, **39**
Sea Beech 30, **31**
Sea Belt 26, **27**
Sea Chervil 52, **53**
Sea Feather 40, **41**
Sea Gooseberry 42, **43**
Sea Hare 84, **85**
Sea Lemon 90, **91**
Sea Lettuce 22, **23**
Sea Mat 52, **53**
Sea Mouse 54, **55**
Sea Oak 24, **25**
Sea Pen 50, **51**
Sea Potato 96, **97**
Sea Snail 112, **113**
Sea Spider 72, **73**
Sea Squirt Mat 100, **101**
Sea Toad 66, **67**
Sea Trout 104, **105**
Securiflustra securifrons 52, **53**
Sepia officinalis 74, **75**
Sepiola atlantica 74, **75**
Serpula vermicularis 58, **59**
Serranus cabrilla 116, **117**
Sertularia argenta 40, **41**
Seven-armed Starfish 94, **95**
Shanny 122, **123**
Shore Clingfish 112, **113**
Short-spined Anglerfish 110, **111**
Short-spined Sea Scorpion 110, **111**
Skeleton Shrimp 73
Small Breadcrumb Sponge 34, **35**
Small Pink Anemone 48, **49**

Small Tube Worm 56, **57**
Small Vase Sponge 34, **35**
Smooth Hound 102, **103**
Smooth Tortoiseshell Limpet 76, **77**
Snake Pipefish 106, **107**
Snakelocks Anemone 44, **45**
Soft Coral Slug 84, **85**
Solaster endeca 94, **95**
Spatangus purpureus 96, **97**
Spinachia spinachia 106, **107**
Spiny Starfish 94, **95**
Spiral Worm 58, **59**
Spiral Wrack 28, **29**
Spirorbis spirorbis 58, **59**
Spotted Cowrie 80, **81**
Spout 82, **83**
Spurdog 102, **103**
Squalus acanthias 102, **103**
Squatina squatina 102, **103**
Squirrel's Tail 40, **41**
Stalked Sea Squirt 98, **99**
Star Ascidian 100, **101**
Strawberry Worm 58, **59**
Strident Squat Lobster 64, **65**
String Jelly 42, **43**
String Vest Sponge 32
Suberites domuncula 32, **33**
Suberites 32, **33**
Sugar Kelp 26
Sunfish 122, **123**
Swiftia pallida 50, **51**
Swimming Crab 68, **69**
Sycon ciliatum 32, **33**
Sygnathus acus 106, **107**
Symphodus melops 118, **119**

Tall Sea Pen 50, **51**
Tangle 24, **25**
Taurulus bubalis 110, **111**
Tectura testudinalis 76, **77**
Thong Weed 24, **25**
Thornback Ray 104, **105**
Thorogobius ephippiatus 120, **121**
Three-bearded Rockling 114, **115**
Three-spined Stickleback 106, **107**
Thuiaria thuja 38, **39**
Thyone fusus 96, **97**
Tompot Blenny 120, **121**

Tonicella marmorea 76, **77**
Tonicella rubra 76, **77**
Toothed Wrack 28, **29**
Topknot 108, **109**
Tortoiseshell Limpet 76, **77**
Tower Shell 80, **81**
Trachinus draco 116, **117**
Tree Sponge 34, **35**
Triglia lucerna 106, **107**
Tritonia hombergi 84, **85**
Tritonia lineate 86, **87**
Trivia arctica 80, **81**
Trivia monacha 80, **81**
Tub Gurnard 106, **107**
Tubularia annulatus 54, **55**
Tubularia indivisa 36, **37**
Tubularia larynx 36, **37**
Turbot 108, **109**
Turret Shell 80, **81**
Turret Shell Anemone 48, **49**
Turritella communis 80, **81**
Tursiops truncatus 124, **125**
Twisted Wrack 28
Two-spot Goby 120, **121**

Ulva lactuca 22
Urn Sponge 32, **33**
Urticina eques 44, **45**
Urticina felina 46, **47**

Variable Tube Worm 58, **59**
Velvet Swimming Crab 70, **71**
Virgularia mirabilis 50, **51**

Warty Sea Fan 50, **51**
White-lined Nudibranch 88, **89**
White-stripe Shrimp 62, **63**
Whiting 114, **115**
Witch 110, **111**
Wolf Fish 122, **123**

Yarrell's Blenny 122, **123**
Yellow Hanging Sponge 34, **35**
Yellow Sunstar 94, **95**
Yellow-tipped Nudibranch 88, **89**

Zeugopterus punctatus 108, **109**
Zostera marina 22, **23**

ACKNOWLEDGEMENTS

Over the years, while collecting the photographs in this book, I have dived with many different groups, dive boats and individuals; it not possible to thank everyone, so I give you a collective 'many thanks'. There are a few individuals that stand out in the crowd. I must pay tribute to my wife Lesley who supports me in all my endeavours, even when it means being away from home to research yet another project: 'Thank you, I really could not do this without you.' Also Sue Scott at Strome; Paul Crowe and the dive boat MV *Topline* at St Abbs in Berwickshire; MV *Bibben* in south-eastern Norway; Ole in Aalborg and Copenhagen, Denmark; Andy Cuthbertson and MV *Jean Elaine* in the Orkney Islands; Joe Rocks in the Shetland Islands.